COMPUTER OUTPUT DESIGN

Computer Output Design

SUSAN WOOLDRIDGE

FIRST EDITION

 PETROCELLI / CHARTER   NEW YORK 1975

Library of Congress Cataloging in Publication Data

Wooldridge, Susan, 1940-
   Computer output design.

   Bibliography: p.
   Includes index.
   1. Computer input-output equipment--Design and con-
struction. 2. Electronic data processing. I. Title.
TK7887.5.W66   001.6'443   75-17672
ISBN 0-88405-308-3

Contents

List of Figures

Acknowledgments

I would like to thank the following companies for their generosity in
supplying information and answering questions:
Atlas Van Lines
Bell & Howell, Ltd.
California Computer Products, Inc.
Cambridge Computer Associates, Inc.
Combined Electronic Services, Ltd.
Computer Related Equipment, Ltd.
Consolidated Analysis Centers, Inc.
Control Data Corporation
Cullinane Corporation
Data Disc, Inc.
DatagraphiX, Inc.
Data Products, Inc.
Dylakor Computer Systems, Inc.
Earth Sciences Research, Inc.
General Electric
Godfrey Systems, Inc.
Hewlett-Packard
Houston Instruments Division of Bausch & Lomb
International Computer Programs, Inc.
Laboratory for Computer Graphics and Spatial Analysis,
    Harvard University
Lamson Paragon
Management Science America, Inc.
McDonnell Douglas Automation Company

National Cash Register Company
National Computing Industries
Pacific Software Services Company
P & O Steamship Company
Pragma, Ltd.
Program Products, Inc.
Randolph Computer Corporation
Softech
Sperry-Univac
System Development Corporation
System Implementation Corporation
Systems Manufacturing Corporation
The Management Group, Inc.
Varian Data Machines
Xynetics, Inc.

Introduction

This book is the companion volume to *Computer Input Design* by the same author. It covers the design of the output subsystem from the point where data are set up in memory for printing or display through delivery to the ultimate user.

The proliferation of paper is a modern business problem to which computers have made a substantial contribution. It has been estimated that in the United States, computers produce five miles of paper for every man, woman, and child in the country every month.

Reports that are produced but never read, and reports that are needed but never produced, are twin phenomenon commonplace in business computer installations. If those are the most severe problems, not far behind is that of reports that should be useful but are not because they are so poorly designed. Finally, there is another type of failure that can be just as serious, although it is not as widely recognized: the production of reports on the line printer when some other form of output would be more useful, faster, or cheaper. This book is intended to draw attention to these problems and to provide a range of practical solutions.

The book is intended as a text, handbook, and reference manual for systems analysts. It is especially aimed at those just beginning their careers in systems analysis, although experienced analysts should find much value, too. It is not a catalog of equipment. The principles of the different types of output devices are explained, but the emphasis is on design techniques. Illustrations, diagrams, and examples are used liberally, and there is a bibliography for further study.

PART ONE

INTRODUCTION

CHAPTER 1

The Output Subsystem

Commercial computer systems, like Gaul, are traditionally divided into three parts: input subsystem, computer subsystem, and output subsystem. These are illustrated in Figure 1.1. Although this segmentation is somewhat artificial, in that no part can be designed or operated in isolation from the others, it is convenient to discuss them as separate units.

The input subsystem includes collection of the data, putting it onto forms of some kind, and turning it into a format that the computer can read. For a conventional batch system, this usually means hand transcription onto punching forms, followed by keypunching onto cards, paper tape, magnetic tape, or disk through a key-to-disk system, and then "take on" or editing and checking of the input by the first computer program. There may be manual checks throughout for legibility, completeness, batch controls, and accuracy. The edit program rejects transactions that are in error; these must be corrected and re-input to the system. The most time-consuming, error-prone, and expensive steps in this process are the hand transcription of source documents and then keying. Two major alternative methods are the use of direct-read documents (mark sensing, optical character recognition, etc.) and on-line input, with the user keying data directly into the computer system through a terminal, usually comprising a keyboard and either a typewriterlike printer or a visual display unit.

The computer subsystem in a business environment consists largely of file handling procedures: updating, matching, merging, sorting, extraction and calculation of data, and printing. Much of this work is performed in whole or in part by preprogrammed routines supplied by

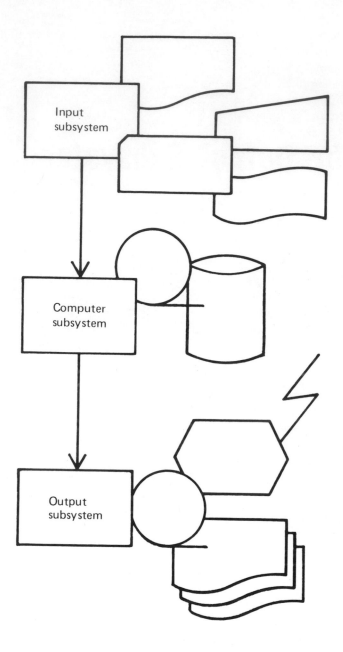

Fig. 1.1 Input, computer, and output subsystems

4

the manufacturer or an independent software house, or written in the installation and used as and when needed by the programmers.

The output subsystem begins at the point where selected data is formatted for human use. By far the largest proportion of computer output is printed on a high-speed line printer directly controlled by the main computer. Variations of this method, which will be discussed in detail in the next chapter and throughout this book, include remote output over long-distance lines, display on a screen, graphic (as opposed to alphanumeric) representation on a plotter or visual display unit, and off-line production from a tape or disk file created by the computer subsystem.

The steps in a typical batch processing output subsystem are shown in Figure 1.2. These include production on the line printer, a quick check for completeness and quality in the computer room by the operator, a more thorough check outside, usually in the data control unit, and then a variety of forms operations. These may include decollating—separation of the parts of a multipart report; bursting—taking the pages apart at the perforations and removing the guide strips; binding into folders; and delivery to the user department. If the output is to be sent to suppliers or customers, procedures for folding, inserting into envelopes, addressing, stamping, and sealing are needed. Some of these manual steps may, of course, be avoided or shortened, for example, by the use of window envelopes and franking with a postage meter. There is a wide range of such possibilities limited only by the ingenuity of the system designer and the cost-benefit breakdown; these will be discussed in detail later in the book. Depending on the use to be made of the output, other steps could be slicing, photocopying with or without reducing, microfilming, and collating.

THE NEED FOR GOOD OUTPUT DESIGN

Output is the most neglected area of system design. A poorly designed report, even if it contains all the information required by the user, may be so difficult to read and interpret that it is worse than useless. So is output delivered too late, after the need for the information has passed. Untidy and illegible forms sent to customers or suppliers can seriously damage the company's image and even its competitive position. A few real-life examples will serve to illustrate how poorly designed output procedures can endanger the value of the entire computer system.

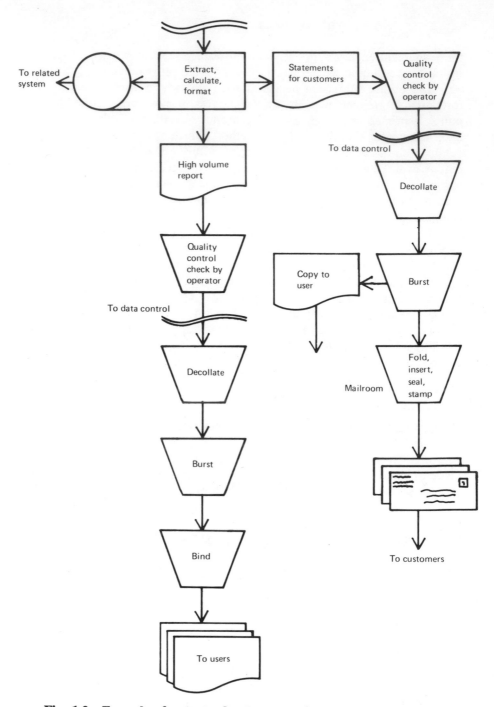

Fig. 1.2 Example of output subsystem procedures

6

The first example falls into the "incredible but true" category of stupid mistakes. The output involved was only a small part of a large inventory control system, which may explain why the system's designers paid so little attention to it. It was required that certain managers be able to interrogate the product master file for details of a product at any time. About 150 line-item requests were expected, at a maximum, in any one day; on-line interrogation could not be justified. A procedure was established whereby a request form was filled out, keypunched, and processed during the daily update. The information required was printed for delivery by five o'clock on the day the request was received, provided it was submitted by noon. This response time was entirely satisfactory to the managers concerned. For the first week of pilot running, these special requests were held back to allow all concerned to concentrate on more important output. On Monday of the second week, therefore, more than 600 requests had accumulated and were processed. The output was delivered to the data control section for bursting and distribution. Only when the data control clerk had 600 bits of paper piled up did he suddenly realize that there was no way to determine which manager should get which replies. The solution was simple, although by this time rather expensive: the name of the manager and his department number had to be keypunched, carried through the system, and printed on the output. This meant a redesign of the request form (scrapping large quantities of forms that had been printed), and redesign and reprogramming at several places in the computer system. The embarrassed systems team had neglected to follow through the design of the output subsystem to its final step, delivery to the users.

In another example the design fault was somewhat more complicated, but had the same cause. The system in question was to produce invoices for customers. Justification for automating the application was largely to improve the company's cash flow position. Under the old system the time lapse between delivery of the goods and receipt of the customer's payment averaged three months. By sending invoices sooner the company hoped to get paid sooner. Systems work went smoothly and the system was installed on schedule. The company accountants sat back and waited for the expected improvement in cash flow, but it did not happen; customers were taking just as long to pay as before. An investigation was held. It was discovered that in the old system, the mail room received invoices to be sent out in dribs and drabs all month. With the new system, they all arrived in one huge batch once a month. It took the boys in the mail room the rest of the month to get them folded, inserted into envelopes, addressed, sealed, and stamped. As happens with some traffic bypasses, the bottleneck had merely been moved from one place to another with no resulting decrease in overall journey time. The cure in this case was not as simple; installing more sophisticated equipment in the mail room wiped out a large portion of the projected cash benefits.

As these examples show, neglect in designing output procedures that must take place *after* the printouts leave the computer room can have very serious consequences. It behooves any professional systems designer to pay as much attention to postproduction procedures as to, say, source document design or file structures.

There are other reasons for taking special pains with this part of the computer system. One is the touchy problem of maintaining, or achieving, a good working relationship between the data processing department and users. It is in the output of computer systems that users have most contact with day-to-day running of the data processing department, and it is by the output that systems are judged. This is especially true of user managers, who are most likely to get and rely on printed reports to guide them in running the company, but it is also true of clerical staff who may be responsible for analyzing error reports and correcting input for resubmission, as well as using file listings to answer inquiries and carry out their jobs. These reports must be up-to-date, on time, and accurate. They must also be legible and easy to read; if they are not, the "intangible" loss to the company of staff time and temper, as well as hostility and resentment toward the data processing department, can more than offset possible benefits of the systems.

Another very serious problem faced by the system designer is that of the growing proliferation of paper in the business world. Computer printers are capable of producing far more paper than it would be possible for human staff to even glance through, much less study with care. Just because something is technologically feasible does not mean it is necessarily desirable. The consequences of designing a system that produces quantities of unnecessary paper range from the extra cost to the company of computer time, stationery, and staff time, to depletion of national forests: Is this report worth the death of a tree? There are many ways in which a clever designer can reduce the quantity of paper used, and they are discussed in detail in this book.

The security of confidential data is another area of concern in designing the output subsystem. It is first necessary to determine whether any of the data in the system would be of potential harm to the organization if it fell into the wrong hands, to determine the degree of risk and the probability of a security breach, and then to design appropriate procedures to prevent or detect a breach. It is a fact that if the system processes confidential data, the risk is more likely to concern output than any other part of the system. Input is "raw data" and not likely to be of use until it is processed; if that were not true, computer processing would be unnecessary. Much time and money is spent in protecting the integrity of files and programs, especially for real-time systems; from the point of view of an industrial spy intent on obtaining access to confidential data, the use of line shielding, Faraday cages, and other electronic antibugging measures are laughable. Why should he try to tap into the computer when he can get what he wants by picking up a copy of a printout from an unattended desk or the trash barrel out back? Protecting hard-copy output is the first line of defense for confidential data. It is the responsibility of the system designer to build in procedures for this protection and to consult with the user in ensuring that they are workable and that their cost is justified by the risk. This problem is discussed in detail in Chapter 18.

Finally, the designer must be concerned with time and money. Getting output to the user fast enough for it to be of value and doing so in the most economic way are his primary tasks. There are a wide variety of output techniques available to choose from; this book is devoted to describing the alternatives available, explaining the choice criteria in each case, and showing how to make the best use of each.

CHAPTER 2

Types of Output

This chapter gives an overview and summary of the material covered in detail in the remainder of the book. It will concentrate on types and classifications of computer output devices and on the types of techniques associated with them.

As a starting point the basic terminology of computer output will be set out and defined. As with many other technical subjects, mastering the jargon is half the battle of understanding the subject matter. Explanations of more specific terminology are given throughout the book in the appropriate places. Although no all-embracing glossary is included in this book, references found in the index will be of use in finding definitions of these terms.

BASIC TERMINOLOGY

Batch. A batch is an accumulation of data to be processed. In batch processing the input data is accumulated for a specific, predetermined interval of time, perhaps a day or a week. At the end of the time period the data is processed by the computer system. The output produced is called "batch output."

Remote. Remote means remote from the main computer center, even from the room in which the computer processing unit (CPU) stands. Remote output could thus be controlled by the central computer but actually take place in the next room or halfway around the world. The connection between the CPU and the remote device could be via cable or the public telephone system.

Hard copy. Hard copy is output printed on a piece of paper as opposed to displayed on a screen. Hard copy is more or less permanent or nontransient—it can be handled, filed, and so on. Microfilm is sometimes included in the category of hard-copy output.

Alphanumeric. Alphanumeric means consisting of alphabetics A–Z, numerics 0–9, and special symbols such as punctuation marks, currency signs, and arithmetic signs. A typical digital computer character set is 64 characters, and most output would be restricted to these characters. They do not usually include lower-case letters.

Graphic. Visual data that is not alphanumeric is called "graphic." Graphic output can be charts, graphs, diagrams, drawings, and so on. Alphanumeric output, as opposed to graphic, is the mainstay of most business data processing systems. This is somewhat unnatural and has been brought about by the much higher speeds and lower costs with which alphanumeric data can be produced on computer output peripherals.

Off-Line. Off-line means not connected with the central computer. Computer output can be easily produced off-line on a special-purpose device. For example, a magnetic tape with data produced by the central computer can be loaded onto an off-line device that consists of a tape reader and a printer. Hard copy for human use is thus produced. There are many other types of off-line devices for handling computer-produced media. Their main advantage is that no CPU time is required for the relatively slow production of hard-copy output.

On-Line. On-line has two general meanings. In the context of computer peripherals, it means any device directly connected to and controlled by the computer, whether remote or not. It also means input, or output, or a combination of both, direct from the source to the central computer system or the reverse. Devices that are on-line in the second sense are always on-line in the first, but not necessarily vice versa.

Real Time. The term "real time" describes a system in which a major portion of both the input and the output are in an on-line mode, with computer processing taking place within the time frame of human work. Submission of prime input data for processing and receipt of the results occur almost concurrently, and input errors may be detected and corrected at the time of entry. Inquiries about data on the computer files may be made as required and the answers displayed or printed at once. The term "real time" is often incorrectly used to describe systems in which only the input is on-line (a data entry system) or only the output (an information retrieval system); in these two types of systems, other processing takes place in a batch mode.

Interactive. Also called "conversational" mode, the interactive type of processing is often based on visual display terminals. The input and output proceed as if they were a conversation, with the terminal operator requesting information and the computer responding. The operator's next request may then be based on the response, for example, in asking for more details of a particular transaction. Graphic displays can also be interactive, with the operator modifying a diagram or drawing and storing the results on computer files for later retrieval. Some specialized systems reverse the procedure, with the computer requesting information and the user responding; one example would be a medical diagnostic system.

Turnaround. Turnaround documents are both input and output at various times in their life cycle. For example, a punched card can be output, handled by humans and perhaps have data added to it, and then returned to the computer system to signal the completion of an event or a series of events, such as the production of an item in the machine shop. Further processing of the data then takes place. Turnaround documents are almost always batch oriented.

Figure 2.1 summarizes the major kinds of output from computer systems in terms of the words defined above. As can be seen the major categories of output identified are batch, remote, real time, graphic, and turnaround. There is, however, some overlap between these categories. Batch output can also be remote; most real-time output is by definition also remote; some devices are suitable for both alphanumeric and graphic output whereas others produce only one or the other; punched cards can be batch, remote, turnaround, or a combination of these. In spite of these many areas of overlap, however, some scheme of classification must be chosen, and the one outlined in Figure 2.1 is the basic scheme used in this book.

The remainder of this chapter is taken up with an overview of the major categories.

HIGH-VOLUME BATCH OUTPUT

High-volume batch output is almost entirely alphanumeric as opposed to graphic. Without doubt the vast majority of computer-produced output falls into this category. Furthermore most of it is produced on a high-speed line printer in the computer room. There are, however, a

A. Batch
   1. High-volume periodic reports
   2. Error and control reports and messages
   3. Masters for multicopy production
   4. Microfilm

B. Remote
   1. Hard copy, high or low volume
   2. Punched cards
   3. Paper tape
   4. Other computer-compatible media and special-purpose output

C. Real Time
   1. Teleprinters
   2. Visual display terminals
   3. Other on-line peripherals and special-purpose devices

D. Graphic
   1. Line printers
   2. Graph plotters
   3. Printer-plotters
   4. Visual display terminals

E. Turnaround
   1. Punched cards
   2. OCR/OMR documents

Fig. 2.1 Types of output

number of different kinds of printers and many models on the market. The characteristics of these, and how they influence systems design, will be discussed in Chapter 4.

It is the restrictions imposed on report design by line printers that lead to grumbling and dissatisfaction on the part of those who must use the output reports. Line printers have only capital letters. Worse, they print one line at a time, leading to the need to make report pages wider than they are long with as much data as possible crammed into one line in order to run the printer at its fastest pace. The limited graphics capability of these devices also impose somewhat artificial restraints on output design.

In spite of their designation as "high-speed," however, line printers are still very slow in relation to internal processing speeds of the computer. One alternative that is gaining in popularity is the use of microfilm. For high-volume batch work, computer output to microfilm (COM) can give considerable savings in faster throughput and cost. Microfilm recorders can be driven by magnetic tape and operate at electronic, as opposed to mechanical, speeds. On the other hand computer output to microfilm is not suitable for volatile data or for real-time processing; it is strictly a replacement for printed batch output. Also, there is the need for additional special equipment. COM cannot replace all printed output. Recorders and processors are expensive items of capital equipment; and there is the need for special viewers for all users of the microfilm.

Microfilm as a computer output medium is discussed in detail in Chapter 9.

REMOTE AND ON-LINE OUTPUT

The terms "remote," "on-line," and "real time" have already been defined. From the point of view of the systems designer, developing an on-line system is significantly different from developing a batch system in two important ways. The first is that the logical complexity of the system and the time span in which it will run require a much closer relationship between input, processing, and output. It is even more difficult to separate these and treat them as distinct subjects for study and specification. The second major difference is that the design of an on-line system requires new and different knowledge and skills from the designer.

An entire section of the book, Part Three, is devoted to real time; there, Chapters 10 and 11 cover the principles of real-time systems and basic definitions of terms associated with on-line networks, data transmission, and communications hardware and software.

The two most widely used on-line input/output devices are teleprinters (also called "teletypewriters") and visual display units. A chapter is devoted to each. A teleprinter is in all essential respects a remote character printer, and can be treated as such for design purposes. A visual display unit (VDU), on the other hand, is not so much a different breed as a new species of creature. It can be used both for data entry and for relatively high-volume output, it provides for both alphanumeric and extensive graphic input and output, and it makes possible a high degree of interaction between the computer system and the user regardless of his geographical distance from the computer center. There are in addition many new types of features for use with a visual display unit that are not associated with any other type of computer peripheral, for example, a light pen.

Just because something is new, different, and technologically interesting, however, does not necessarily mean that it is willy-nilly desirable. The design of a real-time system almost always includes selection of new hardware and software, the terminals being only one of the types of hardware to be considered. The venture can mean a considerable capital outlay on the part of a company. It therefore behooves a systems analyst to make himself as knowledgeable as possible about real time, hardware, software, and design possibilities, and to take great care over selection and design decisions for the new system.

GRAPHIC OUTPUT

The powerful graphics capabilities of visual display units have already been mentioned. There are other devices that will also give the user his information in a graphic format, however, beginning with the high-speed line printer.

Although the graphics capabilities of the line printer are obviously limited, much more can be done with it than is usually the case. Simple charts and graphs can be produced without an overwhelming increase in design and programming complexity, provided the important general guidelines and conventions for this type of output are followed. There are also available a number of software packages that will take as input standard tape and disk file records, massage the data, and produce a variety of graphic outputs under control of parameter cards written by the systems analyst or programmer. The possibilities offered in this area should not be overlooked.

Other graphics devices are plotters and printer-plotters. As the technology improves and costs decrease, these types of devices become more and more a realistic possibility for even entirely commercial organizations. Because of their popularity for scientific and engineering applications, there are more installations every day that possess one of these devices. The business-oriented systems analyst should be familiar with their capabilities.

Part Four of this book covers the mechanics and output design considerations for graphics production from line printers, plotters, and printer-plotters.

Finally, there is a summary of the relative speeds and applicability of the major types of output devices mentioned here in Figure 2.2.

Device	Output Volume	Typical Speed	Remote Use Feasible	Off-line	Real Time Interactive	Graphics Capability
Drum or chain-type line printer	high	600–3,500 lpm	yes	not usually	no	limited
Electrostatic line printer	high	500–6,000 lpm	yes	not usually	no	some models
Electrothermal printer	low–medium	20 lpm	yes	not usually	no	very limited
Ink-jet printer	low–medium	120 lpm	yes	not usually	no	very limited
Dot-matrix (needle) printer	low–medium	150 lpm	yes	not usually	no	very limited
Computer-output microfilm (COM)	high	30,000 lpm	no	tape driven	no	yes
Teleprinter	low–medium	10–120 cps	yes	not usually	yes	very limited
Visual display unit, alphanumeric	low–medium	transmission rate 2,400–9,600 bps	yes	input only	yes	no
Visual display unit, graphic	low–medium	transmission rate 2,400–9,600 bps	yes	no	yes	yes
Flatbed graph plotter	low	1–12 ips	yes	tape driven	special-purpose systems	yes
Drum graph plotter	low–medium	2–26 ips	yes	tape driven	no	yes

lpm = lines per minute
cps = characters per second
bps = bits per second
ips = inches per second

Fig. 2.2 Output summary

CHAPTER 3

Designing the Output Subsystem

This chapter deals briefly with the *process* of systems design as opposed to the *content*. In that systems design is to some extent a creative process, designing a system is often compared with painting a picture. (The debate on how important creativity really is as an attribute of a good systems designer will be left to another time and place.) Books and schools that teach painting concentrate on matters of technique and style; the content or subject of a painting is considered to be entirely at the discretion of the artist. In contrast, books and courses on systems design focus on content—file structures, types of input, and the like—ignoring the creative act of applying knowledge and skills to produce a system. Creativity cannot, of course, be taught, but some of its more easily identifiable hallmarks can be analyzed and discussed, and it is these that this chapter is concerned with.

THE SYSTEM DEVELOPMENT PROCESS

Before narrowing in on the process of designing a system, or of our even more limited target of designing the output subsystem, it is necessary to gain some perspective with a short look at the overall process of developing a commercial computer system in a typical business organization. The steps in the system development process are listed in Figure 3.1. The dividing lines between one step and another and the names given to each may vary from one installation to another; but all commercial computer systems development goes through some variation of this basic pattern.

17

Initiation Phase
   User request and exploratory study
   Feasibility study
     information gathering
     analysis
     design

Implementation Phase
   System design
     information gathering
     analysis
     design
   Programming
   Documentation*
   System testing
   Conversion
   Implementation

Postimplementation Phase
   Maintenance
   Evaluation

* Documentation is shown as a separate step, but it is really a continuous activity throughout systems development.

Fig. 3.1   The steps in systems development

Initiation Phase

First thoughts about a computer system may come from within the data processing department, whose mission includes recognizing such opportunity areas, or from the user or top management of the company, who have identified a problem that computerized data processing may be able to solve. The first documentation is usually a memo or brief report requesting the services of a systems analyst. His work (or the work of his team if the project is a large one) usually takes the form of a feasibility study to analyze the potential costs and benefits of a new system. Ideally the analysis should consider several alternatives, ranging from the "do nothing solution," to a revised manual system, to one or more computer-based systems. Each alternative requires, on a limited scale, gathering of information, analysis, and outline design. It is for each alternative outline design that a cost-benefit analysis is performed. This is a risk venture; the project may be abandoned now, so it is not desirable to spend large sums of money in conducting a feasibility study.

We will assume, however, that a computer solution has been chosen and authorization given for continuing the work. Note that here reality sometimes differs from theory; in many organizations the decision to commit funds for system development is made unilaterally by the data processing department, because it is left to them by default, or because no one else will risk such a decision, or even because the manager is making a power play. The user, directly or indirectly, must pay for the computer system; it should be his decision alone.

Implementation Phase

Now come the major tasks of design and programming. It will probably be necessary to gather more detailed information about present procedures and future requirements than was done at the time of the feasibility study, with a further and more thorough analysis of this information leading to a detailed system design. It is with this design step, particularly as it involves output, that this book is concerned, and the subject will be returned to shortly.

Programming is considered to include detailed logic design, coding, test data preparation, and testing of individual programs and modules to the satisfaction of the programmer and his supervisor.

Documentation, of course, must take place all through the project. A major effort must be put in as programming is finished to record details of how the system and each program work and to set out instructions for the operations department who are to run the system and for users who prepare input and use output.

The systems team now takes over the programs to test the system as a whole, including manual procedures—preparation of input and distribution of output—and linkages between systems. It is at this stage that many data processing departments begin to earn their bad reputations for late delivery and failure to comply with user requirements. Systems testing is rushed to try to make up for previous delays; inevitable requests for modifications and maintenance to the system have to be dealt with one way or another; errors in the original system specification begin to make themselves known; new projects are looming and demand attention. Careful and thorough systems testing is essential. If it is skimped and the system allowed to begin to operate on live data, the coup de grace will be delivered to the reputation and future effectiveness of the data processing department when the user discovers that his expensive new system just does not work. As was pointed out in Chapter 1, failure on testing output procedures is a major part of this syndrome.

Now come the tasks of converting data to computer files and implementing the new system. In fact, planning and work on these steps should have begun very early in the project, with initial plans included in the feasibility study refined and made more detailed throughout systems design and programming. A parallel or pilot implementation may be chosen, or if these are unsuitable because of cost, a gradual phasing in of the new system. As a last resort a sudden cutover from the old system ("immediate implementation") to the new may be required.

Postimplementation Phase

The system is not, however, complete, nor will it ever be. Changes in the company's business, in its competitive position, in the policy of its management, or in legal requirements may all necessitate changes to the computer system. Furthermore, new hardware and new software brought in by the data processing department may make changes desirable and necessary. Modifications to improve operating performance or user satisfaction will also have to be made. An optimistic point of view is to call this maintenance "improvements" or "enhancements," although too often it is really bug chasing that should have been done before implementation.

In a well-managed data processing department, postimplementation evaluations will be carried out at regular intervals on all operational systems. This exercise leads to further improvements and enhancements to the system. It is also a valuable learning tool, a means of identifying mistakes in order to avoid repeating them in future systems.

Information Gathering

The success of the output subsystem, and to a great extent the degree of user satisfaction with the completed system, depends heavily on the thoroughness with which information gathering is carried out. Figure 3.2 lists the major categories of information required, particularly as they relate to designing output.

The user must be consulted about his requirements for the new system. A good starting point, of course, is the data produced at present, that is, the information and reports currently available to him whether prepared by hand or through a computer system. Samples should be

For the feasibility study:
   Objectives for the system
   Outline of required output
   Problems with the present system
   Types of data available for processing
   Where and in what environment the data originated
   Hardware and data handling equipment; present and expected future
      workloads

For detailed system design:
   All of the above plus:
   Sample of all forms and reports prepared at present
     For each one:
       who prepares it
       who uses it and for what
       what is on it
       number of copies
       volumes: peaks, troughs, growth rate
       time cycles
   Specifications of hardware and equipment

Fig. 3.2   Information to be gathered

gathered of all of these. All present and potential users should be questioned about their satisfaction with the present output, what they like and want to continue to receive, what is missing and would be useful to them for the future, and in what ways current output is unsatisfactory and could be improved. The systems analyst must listen carefully, take notes, and encourage each person to go into as much detail as possible.

If the computer system is breaking new ground, that is, if there is no equivalent manual system and much or all of the output is not now being produced, the investigation of user requirements must be even more carefully done. If the computer system will be introducing a new technique such as automated inventory control or optimization of transport, the systems analyst and the user may be starting from the same point, that is, total ignorance of the possibilities and pitfalls. Research and education become a larger part of the data processing department's job and may require an extensive study phase involving visits to other companies and close liaison with user groups, the computer manufacturer, and software suppliers. In such a situation the new system must be designed with a degree of flexibility usually not found on systems that merely replicate the old manual system (for example, payroll) so that as practical experience is gained, modifications and improvements to the output produced can be made with a minimum of effort.

USER CHECKPOINTS

It is essential to build into the design process a series of formal checkpoints where users and management are given the opportunity to review the design, particularly that of output; request changes; and authorize further work. Two major checkpoints should come after completion of the feasibility study and after completion of system design before programming begins. A series of lesser checkpoints are needed during analysis and design.

For each of these checkpoints, the user should see the output design, including report layouts and procedures of the output subsystem. However, he should *not* be given printer layout forms; those are for programmers. If at all possible, the analyst should create dummy reports that are exact replicas (if of fewer pages) of what the real output will look like. The same approach can be used for the other types of output, including checks, turnaround documents, error listings, and so on. To make these samples as realistic as possible, actual figures can be used so that the results are meaningful to the user in his own terms. If the department does not have a utility program to create dummy output from cards, a wide choice is available from the commercial software market at reasonable prices (see Appendix A). The only exception may be preprinted forms not yet ordered. The user can be shown artwork or at least a mock-up of what the finished design will look like, and his final approval must be obtained before an order is placed.

WORKING TO SPECIFICATION

As detailed design gets underway, the systems team will begin to see more and more possibilities for additional output. The major outputs specified in the feasibility study may be just a starting point; given the input and the data held on master files, a further range of possible output reports becomes evident. It is important to exercise some restraint in this matter.

If the new computer system is an exact replica of the old system, there will be less room for expansion of output and the user will have more definite ideas about what he wants. If the system is breaking new ground, however, and especially if the user has not had previous experience with computer systems and in working with the data processing department, it will be relatively easy to convince him of the desirability of additional reports. Always keep in mind the axiom that even if it is technologically possible, it is not necessarily desirable. A novice computer user must start slowly, learning as he goes, without being led to committing himself to a system larger and more expensive than one he really needs. Those unfamiliar with computers do not have an appreciation of the volume of paper that can be produced from fast line printers.

On the other hand this is not to say that the systems team should not suggest useful output to the user. Especially if he is new to computer usage, he may be unaware of possibilities. However, it is the user's system and his output; and he must be more knowledgeable about his business and its requirements than the systems designer.

CYCLICAL NATURE OF SYSTEMS DESIGN

The traditional approach to systems design is to start with the output specification and work backward, designing the computer files and the computer processing, and then designing the input media and source documents. This seems logical because the output requirements can be specified first, and authorized, before other parts of design are begun. Certain difficulties may arise, however; by the time input design is started, the rest of the system is fixed and numerous alternatives will have been automatically ruled out. There will be less flexibility possible.

Another approach is to begin with the computer subsystem and proceed to input or output afterward. This is suitable for large data base systems in which the most important criterion is to allow flexibility for the future. For less ambitious systems, however, it can lead to an overbalance in favor of operational efficiency to the detriment of ease of use for human beings who must prepare input and use output.

A third alternative is to design from the top down, working from the input subsystem through the computer subsystem to the output.

Although this may seem logical to those not experienced in systems design, it has the very real danger that the input required to create output will be overlooked until much work has been done, work that then has to be scrapped.

It is more realistic to think of systems being designed in a circular way. As with a painting, a rough outline of the whole is first sketched, with details gradually being added, first to one part of the canvas and then to another. Essential output is specified, and trial versions of master files to produce it are set up. The input needed to create these files is then identified, and means of getting it into the computer system are postulated. This in turn may lead to a redesign of the computer subsystem and alterations to the output. Finally, a satisfactory picture is completed, each part in balance with the others and all details just right.

A change anywhere in the system will cause the need for variation somewhere else, as in the plate of spaghetti principle: when something on one side of the plate is moved, you never know what is going to move on the other side.

DESK TESTING THE SYSTEM

As the system begins to take shape, the designer should document all ideas and decisions. Nothing is more frustrating than to think of a solution to a problem and then because of an interruption or a delay, to lose it again. This is doubly important if the design work is being done by more than one person, a team. The best approach in that case is to draw trial designs on a blackboard, copying them to flowchart paper as details are agreed on; but a room should never be left unoccupied with the only documentation on the blackboard.

As each section, or version, of the design is completed, it should be "tested" by walking through, just as a programmer desk checks the logic of coding. Types of improvements that may be possible are

1. Logic debugging
2. Rationalization—combining two or more steps into one
3. Simplification—eliminating steps
4. Improving speed of operation, manual and computer
5. Improving acceptability to users
6. Tightening security (see Chapter 18)

A summary of test questions to be applied to the system is given in Figure 3.3.

For each data item:
 Is it either present on a master file, or can be derived from items
  present?
 Can it be derived from something else before printing?
 Is it essential in any case?
 Could it be replaced by a code or an abbreviation?
 Should it be expanded to be more meaningful?

For each output:
 Is it essential?
 Could it be improved for the user?
 Are there enough copies?
 Are all copies essential?
 How could printing be speeded up?
 What off-line steps are required?
 When and how will it reach the user?

For each off-line step:
 Could this step be eliminated or combined with something else?
 How long will it take?
 Could it be speeded up?

Fig. 3.3   Desk checking the system design

PART TWO

HIGH-VOLUME BATCH OUTPUT

CHAPTER 4

Printers

This section of the book is devoted to batch (as opposed to on-line) output production methods and design and is primarily concerned with alphanumeric (as opposed to graphic) types of output. It is into this category that by far the largest proportion of computer-produced output falls and with which most systems analysts will be concerned in developing ordinary or garden variety commercial batch systems that form the bulk of those that will become operational in this decade, and probably well into the next. This chapter is about high-speed printers, the computer peripheral device that produces most hard-copy output. The following chapters in this section cover the design of the output, and the off-line operations required to prepare it for human consumption. The final chapter of this section covers the other major batch output method, computer output microfilm. Remote on-line and graphic output are discussed later.

There has been a proliferation of new types and models of computer printers made available in the last few years. New ones appear on the market so frequently that it seems almost futile to try to know details of all of them. The systems designer should know what the major types are and how they work, and be familiar with the more important technical terminology. Operational details and specifications can then be readily acquired from sales literature and manufacturers' technical manuals as needed.

There are a number of different ways of classifying the types of computer printers on the market. A summary will be found in Figure 4.1. Two major divisions may be seen in serial (one character at a time) printers versus line printers, and impact versus nonimpact printers.

Type of Printer	Impression Method	Impression Rate	Speed Range
Chain	Impact	Line	200–3500 lpm
Drum	Impact	Line	200–2000 lpm
Electrostatic	Nonimpact	Line	500–6000 lpm
Electrothermal	Nonimpact	Character	30 cps, 20 lpm
Ink-jet	Nonimpact	Line or character	120 lpm
Xerographic	Nonimpact	Line, character or possibly page*	Unknown*
Dot-matrix	Impact	Line or character	100–600 cps, 125–600 lpm

* See text.

Fig. 4.1   Types of computer printers

As a general rule of thumb, serial printers are much slower than line printers; typewriters and console typewriters are serial printers, for example. Many on-line terminals are serial printers, and these will be discussed in Part Three. For direct high-volume output in the computer room, a faster device is usually required, that is, a line printer. Also, as a generality, nonimpact printers are newer and there is a very wide variety of types. Impact line printers are by far the most popular for high-volume commercial output, and so will be described first.

HIGH-SPEED IMPACT LINE PRINTERS

High Speed. The term "high speed" is relative when used in connection with printers, as indeed it is for most other types of computer peripherals. In second-generation days, 600 lines per minute (lpm) was fast for a printer; today, a 600-lpm device is at the very bottom of the fast range, or at the top of the slow range, depending on the classification system used. The upper limit of speed that the industry is able to produce, at the time of writing, is about 3500 lpm. No doubt the technology will improve still further to extend this limit. Most high-speed printers in use today operate in the range of 1000 to 2000 lpm. It should be noted that these figures, especially when quoted by equipment manufacturers, are the rated speeds, that is, the fastest possible rate obtainable. As will be seen, achieving the rated speed under operational conditions as opposed to test laboratory conditions can be difficult. "High speed" is a relative term in another sense, too. Even the fastest line printers are still the slowest high-volume peripherals in use, a fact that has considerable influence on the design of output systems, the organization of programs, and computer scheduling within the operations department.

Impact. The term "impact" means that the printing is done by hitting metal type characters against the paper, or hitting the paper against the type, with a carbon ribbon in between. Ordinary paper can be used, and a number of copies can be made simultaneously via carbon paper or coated paper. (Types of papers and forms for printing will be discussed in detail in the next chapter.) There are two major types of impact line printers: chain-train and drum. Their operation will be described below.

Line. The term "line" means that an entire line can be printed at once, or effectively so. This requires a control unit and buffer between the printer and the CPU, so that an entire line can be accepted from main store under command of the program that is running. In most medium-to-large multiprogrammed computers the print lines formatted by the problem program are in fact written to disk or tape for output by a utility program at the convenience of the operations department's scheduler.

Chain Printers

The mechanics of chain printers are illustrated in Figure 4.2. The characters are on embossed metal slugs linked together to form an endless loop. The chain is horizontal, with paper passing vertically between it and the bank of hammers. There is one hammer for each of the possible print positions on the line; depending on the device, there can be 80 to 200 print positions; 132 is typical. The chain moves continuously, with the hammers coming up to meet the required characters on the fly, under direction of a built-in control unit that interprets the digital format of the print line received from the CPU. The time lapse between the command to the hammer and its impact is compensated for by firing the hammer just before the desired character reaches the print position.

In the meantime the paper (usually continuous forms) is fed between the ribbon and the hammers by pinwheels that engage the sprocket holes provided on each side of the paper. The pinwheel tractors are adjustable horizontally to accommodate forms of various widths. The sprocket holes can be in perforated margins for later removal. The paper is fed up in one-line increments, also under direction of the control unit, which in turn is receiving commands from the program

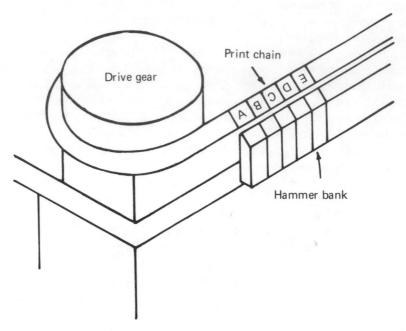

Fig. 4.2   Chain printer components

resident in store. The feed mechanism is controlled by a loop of punched paper tape, so that the paper can be skipped up two, three, or more lines at a time, or can be skipped to the first print line of a new page, in one motion. This is referred to as "high-speed eject," because the movement of the paper can be much faster when nothing is being printed than when feeding must be done in one-line increments. One of the system designer's tasks, when laying out the form, is to specify the carriage control loop format, especially when nonstandard stationery is being used.

There is some choice of the character set on the chain. Chains can be changed between jobs, but this is seldom done. Most installations are content with a standard 64-character set. If it is possible to limit the characters to numerics only, the set can be repeated more often around the chain. This means that the time lapse in waiting for the desired character to appear opposite the hammer is reduced and the speed of printing can be increased. Most commercial applications, however, require a full alphanumeric character set.

Drum Printers

The basic components of a drum or barrel printer are illustrated in Figure 4.3; a photograph is shown in Figure 4.4. As with a chain,

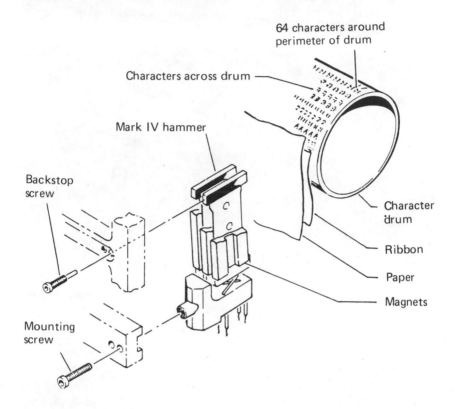

Fig. 4.3 Drum printer components. The Data Products Mark IV hammer printing technique (Courtesy Data Products International, Inc.)

the drum revolves continuously at high speed while the printer is in operation. Printing is done by firing the hammer just as with a chain printer. The time at which a hammer is fired determines the character to be printed. If a line of all X's is required, all print hammers will fire simultaneously. In contrast, with a chain printer all X's would cause a ripple effect, but a line requiring one each of the entire character set, in order, would result in all hammers of the chain printer firing at once.

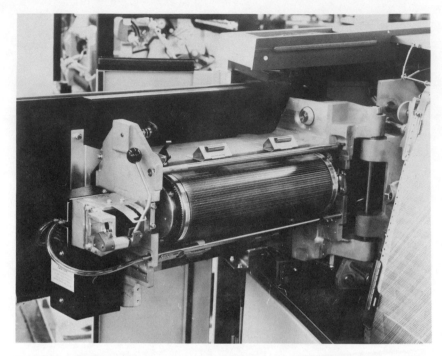

Fig. 4.4 Drum printer. Open view of Data Products 2440 hinged drum gate assembly (Courtesy Data Products International, Inc.)

A misalignment of the mechanism will result in characters of uneven height. Misalignment of a chain printer, on the other hand, gives unequal spacing between characters, which is less discernible to the human eye. This is one factor that accounts for the relative popularity of chain over drum printers. Another is that uneven character heights are likely to result in misreads by optical character readers when printed output is used as turnaround documents (see Chapter 17.)

A problem that both drum and chain printers are heir to, in addition to that of uneven characters, is smearing. The character slug remains in contact with the paper for a definite, although limited, time; but the chain or drum is still moving, so to avoid smearing the ink the hammer dwell time must be very short. A properly set-up and regularly maintained printer, however, will give printouts of acceptable quality through five or six copies, depending on the weight of the paper.

Restrictions imposed by impact line printers are the upper limit on speed and susceptibility to mechanical breakdown, due to the many moving parts; their size; and their noisiness—although the latter can be somewhat reduced by lowering a hood over the device while it is running. For the majority of commercial installations, however, these disadvantages are more than outweighed by the relatively low cost per line or per character printed, the facility of obtaining more than one copy at a time, and the ability to use ordinary fanfold paper without the need for special coatings or chemicals.

NONIMPACT PRINTERS

There are a number of different types of nonimpact printers on the market, each one aiming to overcome one or more of the drawbacks of impact printers. As was mentioned, the relatively low speed of the impact printer in relation to CPU speeds is a serious limitation. If faster devices can be developed that still offer all the advantages of ordinary paper and low cost, the days of the impact printer will be numbered. The technology is developing rapidly in this field, so the discussion below must be taken as a summary of the state of the art as of the time of writing.

It is more convenient to classify nonimpact printers by the method of forming the print image on paper than by dividing them into the two groups of line versus serial printing. These methods are electrostatic or matrix, electrothermal, ink jet, and optical or xerographic. Each will be described in turn. There are variations within these.

Electrostatic Printers

Electrostatic printers, also called "matrix printers," use specially coated paper on which electrostatic charges are placed via conducting nibs, then developed with a liquid toner. The operating principle is illustrated in Figure 4.5.

The electrostatic charge is applied to the special paper by a writing head containing a row of stationary electrodes, equidistant nibs. A small voltage charge to selected nibs places the charge on the paper with the aid of a rear or backup electrode behind the paper. An entire line is "scanned" at once, without movement of either the head or the paper. A close-up of the writing head can be seen in Figure 4.6. Typically, there are 72.5 to 160 nibs per inch. The paper is then spaced up for the next line and as it is ejected from the printer, a liquid toner is applied to develop the image. This is then dried with an air stream. The

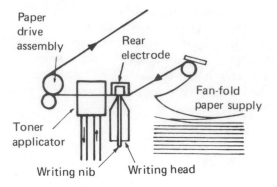

Fig. 4.5   Operating principle of matrix printer (Courtesy Vesatec)

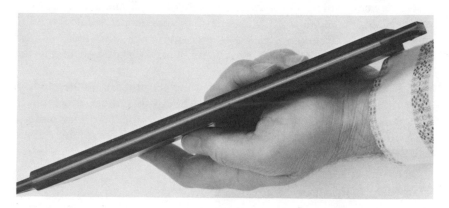

Fig. 4.6   Electrostatic printer writing head (Courtesy Versatec)

only moving parts in the actual writing process are a small pump for circulating the toner and the blower for drying it.

The charges on the paper are in the form of small dots so close together that to the human eye they seem to form lines and curves. The type font is smaller than that of impact printers, so a standard 132-character print line can be accommodated on 11 by 8½ inch paper. An example character set, actual size, is shown in Figure 4.7. Note that it includes lower-case characters, giving the printer a decided plus factor over impact printers for some applications.

The coated paper is more expensive than plain paper. Either fan-

---

ABCDEFGHIJKLMNOPQRSTUVWXYZ

abcdefghijklmnopqrstuvwxyz

0123456789

[\ ] ∧ _ ! " # $ % & ' ( ) * + , − . ∕ { | } ∼ ■ : ; < = > ? @

Fig. 4.7 Electrostatic printer character set. Courtesy Versatec.

fold or roll paper can be used. Roll paper usually comes in 500 or 1000 foot rolls. Figure 4.8 shows a roll being loaded into the device.

The disadvantages of electrostatic printers, compared to impact printers, range from major to trivial. An example of the latter is that there is a delay of a fraction of a second between the time the line is printed and when it can be viewed. More serious drawbacks are the inability to make multiple copies (although the printout can be reproduced on an office copier), the higher cost of the paper, and the necessity of keeping a stock of liquid toner and refilling the machine.

The advantages of electrostatic printers, however, can be considerable. Speeds at the low end of the range are similar to those of impact printers, for example, 500 to 600 lpm; but at the upper end, some electrostatic printers can deliver 5000 to 6000 lpm. Another major advantage is the proven reliability of the equipment—because there are few moving parts, breakdowns are infrequent. Further, because there is no impact, there is no noise, which is an important point for some installations. Finally, the design makes graphical output a possibility; this will be discussed further in Part Four.

Electrothermal Printers

Electrothermal printers also produce matrix characters on specially coated paper, but in this case the image on the paper is produced by heat, literally burning away the outer coating. The technique requires a stylus, or a group of styli, in contact with the paper. The tips are heated by electric current and must heat and cool rapidly to give a reasonable quality of image. The printers are character machines, with the thermal matrix head of styli moving along the print line.

The advantages of electrothermal printers are silence, reliability, and low cost. The disadvantages include the need for special paper

Fig. 4.8 Electrostatic printer setup (Courtesy Versatec)

and a burning smell while the machine is in operation; but the major drawback for many users is the slow speed, typically 30 characters per second (cps), 20 lpm. They are therefore most widely used in small minicomputers or linked to remote visual display units.

Ink-Jet Printers

Ink-jet printers, familiarly known as "ink spitters," are character printers, although some types form two characters at a time. The ink is not the same as ordinary fountain pen ink, and is more properly called the "writing liquid." The writing head consists of one or more nozzles. The droplets of ink are electrically charged and therefore can be deflected by an electric field to fall at the appropriate spot on the paper. Characters are formed by a matrix of drops. The ink reaches the nozzles via capillary action from a reservoir.

In one type of ink-jet printer there are 40 nozzles, each capable of printing two adjacent characters by deflecting the nozzle for an 80-character print line. In another type there is one nozzle in a recording head that moves horizontally across the print line. The characters are formed from the bottom up and have a slanted shape because as the nozzle is moving up, it is also moving sideways.

The advantages of ink-jet machines are that they are quiet, use plain paper, and give a good-quality printout. Drawbacks are the low speed—around 120 lpm—and their inability to give multiple copies. The ink used must be fast drying on the paper but liquid in the nozzles; the structure of the plumbing system and possible clogging of the mechanism lead to relatively low reliability.

Xerographic Printers

Xerographic printers are the newest of techniques for high-speed computer printout. Between the time this is being written and publication day, it is expected that one or more large manufacturers will announce high-speed printers based on the xerographic process. Although the technology has existed for some years in the form of document copiers, the problems of reproducing characters from digital computer signals and doing so very rapidly and cheaply via xerography have prevented this method from being competitive until now.

The process uses a selenium drum on to which the desired image is projected. By means of a photoconductor, the optical image is changed into electrical impulses. Dry toner, fine black carbon particles, is spread over the drum and the particles adhere to the charged areas.

The toner image is transferred to a piece of paper and then fixed in place by heat. The process is fast and cheap and gives high-quality reproduction. Linking the photocopier to a computer and initiating the process with digital signals instead of optical ones, a breakthrough expected soon, will possibly produce a high-speed printer to rival those that now dominate the market.

Dot-matrix Printers

Dot-matrix machines are technically impact printers, some being character printers and others line printers, thus defying tidy classification. They are also called "needle printers" because of the way in which characters are formed.

In character printers the matrix of needles is mounted in a writing head that moves along the print line. Each character is formed by a matrix of dots 5×7 or 7×9. An inked nylon ribbon between the needles and the paper makes the impression. Up to five carbon copies can be made. Figure 4.9 is a sample of dot-matrix output; the matrix

ABCDEFGHIJKLMNOPQRSTUVWXYZ 1234567890
abcdefghijklmnopqrstuvwxyz 1234567890
ABCDEFGHIJKLMNOPQRSTUVWXYZ 1234567890
abcdefghijklmnopqrstuvwxyz 1234567890

CENTRONICS MODEL 101AL

ABCDEFGHIJKLMNOPQRSTUVWXYZ 1234567890
abcdefghijklmnopqrstuvwxyz 1234567890
ABCDEFGHIJKLMNOPQRSTUVWXYZ 1234567890
abcdefghijklmnopqrstuvwxyz 1234567890

Fig. 4.9 Sample dot-matrix output (Courtesy Centronics Data Computer Corp.)

principle is shown in enlarged form in Figure 4.10. A popular dot-matrix printer is illustrated in Figure 4.11.

Fig. 4.10 Example of dot-matrix characters, enlarged

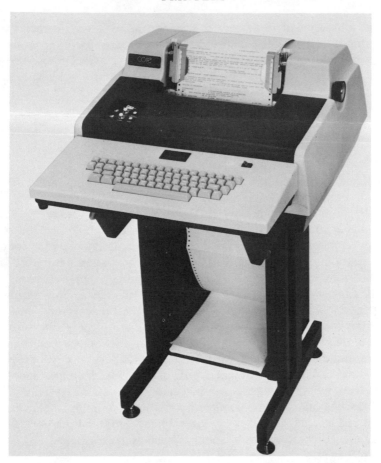

Fig. 4.11   Dot-matrix printer (Courtesy Centronics Data Computer Corp.)

Speeds range from 100 to 600 cps. Calculating lines per minute depends on the length of the line and the number of characters actually printed, but speeds of up to 200 lpm can be reached by the fastest machines.

Dot-matrix line printers use a single-piece comb with hammers, one hammer for each print position. The characters are formed by repeated "blows" of the hammer as paper moves by. There are various matrices, including 5×7, 6×8, 7×9, and 9×9. Line length varies from 80 to 132 characters, depending on the device. Standard 64-character sets are available. Speeds range from 125 to 500 lpm.

As can be guessed from the speed ranges given, dot-matrix

printers are designed to fit into the market above slow character impact printers (typewriters) and below high-speed impact line printers. They give multiple copies and use ordinary paper, overcoming some of the disadvantages of electrothermal and electrostatic printers. Also, they are fairly quiet in operation. Applications include minicomputer systems, hard-copy output associated with visual display units, and key-to-disk system output printers.

SPOOLING

The problems created by line printers or other relatively low-speed devices on-line to large third-generation computers can be partially overcome with a software technique called "spooling." "Spool" is an acrynom for "simultaneous peripheral operation on-line." The print program does not write directly to the printer, but instead writes print-line images to a designated disk or tape file. In a separate partition under multiprogramming, another program reads from this file and writes to the printer. Therefore even if there is only one printer, two or more programs with printed output can run simultaneously. The delay in printing can range from unnoticeable to several days, depending on how much work has been previously stacked on the spooling file and on the organization of the multiprogramming system. This technique, like others made possible by multiprogramming, makes more efficient use of the hardware by overlapping input/output and CPU operations. The best-known spooling system is IBM's HASP.

SELECTION CRITERIA

Before closing this discussion of the different types of computer-output printers on the market, there should be a note about the considerations for choosing a printer or a group of printers. The feasibility study for selecting hardware will probably encompass more than just hard-copy printers; but even if a main-frame computer is being chosen, many of the devices described in this chapter are "plug compatible"; interface hardware and software are available as needed to link these printers to the computers of most manufacturers.

In addition to the obvious factors of cost and speed, the systems analyst should investigate and take into consideration the following:

1. Volume of printing to be done per day, per week, per month
2. Frequency of printing (continuous or intermittent)
3. Type of paper required, including size
4. Environmental factors such as available space and the acceptable noise level

CHAPTER 5

Designing High-Volume Reports

Information means paper on which to print it, and computer-processed information usually means high-speed line printers and continuous forms. The chronic worldwide shortage of paper must be due at least in part to the growing use of computers. It has been estimated that in Europe and North America, up to 75 percent of all paper consumed by business is computer stationery. Five hours of printing by one computer printer on standard four-part paper uses up one tree. Moreover, much of what is produced is thrown away unread or is so poorly designed that it is almost impossible to read and understand. In spite of this most computer output for human use is still printed on continuous forms by a high-speed line printer, usually a chain or drum type described in the last chapter. Alternative output methods are described elsewhere in this book; this chapter is devoted to ways in which to get useful, well-designed output from the line printer at the lowest cost, using the minimum necessary amounts of paper.

A careful study of the users' requirements is necessary before report design can begin; this should have been done in the earlier stages of the project. If the computer system is to produce the same output as that in use at present, the design exercise will be one of adapting existing formats to the characteristics of the line printer. It is more likely that at least some of the output required will be new, and this means that if the new reports are to be useful, the designer must have a thorough understanding of the data to be printed and how it will be used.

Information gathering was discussed in Chapter 3 with checklists of the categories of information required. The user should be consulted regularly throughout the design process (preferably at predetermined

44

checkpoints) about the trial designs that have been drawn up. It is essential to ensure that the reports will contain the information he needs, and only that information, in the most usable format. More specific recommendations for user checkpoints will be given at the end of the chapter.

CONTINUOUS STATIONERY

The first design choice is that of the paper to be used for the reports. Most printers take continuous forms folded accordion style, as illustrated in Figure 5.1. The paper may be single or multipart, using

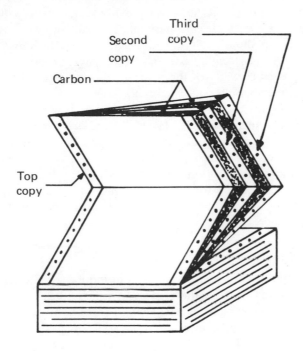

Fig. 5.1 Multipart continuous forms

interleaved carbons, carbon coating, or chemical reaction paper for the copies, either plain (stock) or preprinted to order. The paper must conform to certain minimum requirements of quality and to minimum and maximum size limitations. Within these restrictions, however, there is a wide range of choices to be made.

Quality of the Paper

The printer manufacturer's manual should be consulted for paper quality specifications. The weight of the paper, the amount of the paper dust it contains, and dimensional stability are all important.

Most manufacturers recommend weights in the range of 60 to 85 grams per square meter (gm^2). The paper must be strong enough to be processed by the printer and by ancillary equipment without tearing. On the other hand heavy paper will limit the number of legible copies that can be made. Cost will be a consideration, too.

Dust and debris left in the forms after their manufacture can present serious difficulties. Paper dust can foul the printer mechanism and cause frequent mechanical breakdowns. If the situation is really bad, the dust can affect the air conditioning units and other computer equipment. Optical readers, for example, are particularly sensitive to high levels of dust and debris in the air. Trying to pinch pennies by buying cheap paper with a high dust content is a false economy.

The weight and quality of the paper is also important for legibility and handling. Inexpensive paper tends to have a shiny, greasy surface that is unpleasant to touch and difficult to read. Heavy paper with a matte finish gives much more legible results and is nicer to handle, but will also be more expensive. The decision has to be made taking both cost and user acceptance into consideration. As a general rule forms going out of the company to customers or suppliers should be of reasonable quality; the quality for user acceptance within the company can only be determined in light of company standards, environment, and previous experience.

Multipart Forms

Many output reports will be required in more than one copy. During the investigation stage of the project, it will be necessary to determine how many copies will be needed and for whom and to be sure that each copy is really required; careful study may show that some copies can double up. For example, if one copy is wanted for filing for legal reasons in long-term storage, and will not be referenced, could one of the users contribute his for this purpose when he is finished with it? Or is it possible to do away with the file copy altogether if a master file on magnetic tape would serve the same legal purpose? On the other hand each necessary copy must be identified. Every copy made should be a necessary one and every necessary copy should be made.

The choice of copying method depends on factors of cost and usage. The three main types are one-time carbon paper, coated paper, and chemical reaction paper. It is also possible to get patch or stripe carbon for copying of selected areas only.

Carbon Papers. One-time interleaved carbon paper is the cheapest and the most widely used. The weight and quality of the carbon paper should be matched with the weight of the paper, to ensure the best copies. Continuous stationery printers who supply standard stock multipart forms will already have arranged this marriage. The major drawback of one-time carbon is the extra step required to remove it during decollating of the parts, a messy and time-consuming operation.

Part-coated carbon paper can be used to permit only certain areas of printing to be transferred to lower copies, masking out confidential or unnecessary data. Interleaved carbon paper is manufactured by running a long reel of light-weight paper through a coating machine. It is therefore easier to coat in vertical strips than in horizontal ones. Patches of carbon can be applied, too, but these will be more difficult to produce and thus more expensive than stripes. In spite of the extra cost of the carbon paper, however, this method can still be cheaper and faster than having two separate print runs.

Coated Papers. Coated papers employ a mechanical method of transfer of the print image. The coating is on the underside of the top copy and on the undersides of all subsequent sheets but the last. It is permanent, with the coating (usually gray) clearly visible on the back of the sheet. This can make the paper unpleasant to handle, and there is always the danger of accidental marking after the printing is finished. This type of copying does, however, eliminate the extra step of removing one-time carbon.

Chemical Reaction Papers. Chemical reaction papers also do away with the disadvantage of removing one-time carbons. The image is produced through an interaction between different chemical coatings, one on the back of the sheet above and one on the surface of the receiving sheet. The pressure of the print hammer hitting the paper induces the chemical reaction to form the image. Middle papers in a multipart set have both coatings for up to five copies. This type of paper has a number of other disadvantages in addition to that of extra cost. One of them is that the paper is unpleasant to touch; another is the possibility of accidental stray marks in use. A more serious disadvantage for some applications is the relatively low shelf life of the paper, especially in hot places. Printout left on the windowsill in the sun may become illegible in a matter of days. If the paper is stored under ideal temperature-controlled conditions, legibility may last up to two years. Until recently, photocopying was difficult or impossible because the image produced was blue, a color "invisible" to some office photocopiers. Paper producing a black image is now available, however. This, coupled with a gradual equalization of prices with one-time carbon, is making the chemical reaction type more attractive and more popular for many installations.

Legibility Tests. When choosing a multipart paper, it is vital to run tests for the legibility of the copies. Stationery suppliers should provide samples of the forms being considered, and these must be run on the equipment to be used to be certain that all copies will be legible. Reliance should not be placed on the word of either the printer manufacturer or the forms salesman. The test pack can be run on the computer printer and on any other machine to be used, for example, a typewriter if hand-typed information is to be added to the forms as a later step. If the equipment is not yet installed, the hardware salesman should be able to make time available on an identical unit, either at another installation or at the showroom.

Labels

Continuous stationery is also available in the form of labels for names and addresses or other "stick on" data. The labels can be gummed or pressure sensitive. In either case a variety of standard sizes is available. Depending on the width of each label, it is usually possible to print them two-up, three-up, or more. This means that the sheet of labels has two, three, or more across. Because line printers print a fixed maximum number of lines a minute, the more labels there are "up," the faster the job is. For example, on a 600-lpm printer, 12,000 four-line names and addresses would take 1 hour and 20 minutes (not including eject time) if printed one-up, 40 minutes printed two-up, 20 minutes printed four-up, and so on. Setting up the print lines merely requires a bit of thought at programming time.

If gummed labels are used, they have to be divided along the perforations, dampened, and stuck on. The continuous forms must be clearly marked, or the computer operators must have good instructions for setting up the job; otherwise, it is likely that the printing will be on the gummed side of the paper or on top of the perforations.

Labels also come as multipart forms. The second and subsequent copies can be either more labels or plain paper to provide a master list. If pressure-sensitive labels are used, the number of legible copies will be limited because of the double thickness of label and backing paper.

PREPRINTED FORMS

The use of the same stock stationery for many different printing jobs has several advantages. First, plain paper is less expensive than preprinted forms, and large orders give economies of scale. Second, the computer operator's time is saved because the printer does not need adjusting between jobs, and the number of paper changes is reduced. Finally, handling, binding, and filing methods can be standardized for similar savings in the data control and the user departments.

Some jobs require the use of preprinted forms nonetheless. There are two sets of factors that can lead to the choice of preprinting, and they can operate singly or together. The first includes appearance and company image. Preprinting allows the use of different sizes and styles of type, color, and graphic material such as the company trademark, all of which improve the look of the form and the receptivity of the user. The second is of a different order, but no less important: the possibility of saving considerable printing time by preprinting headings and other constant information. Associated with this is the additional possibility of saving paper with smaller type sizes, column lines between print positions to indicate decimal points, and the like.

Two example preprinted forms have been chosen to illustrate some of the possible options. The variations shown are by no means the only ones available but will serve to indicate some of the types of paper and preprinting available. Specific comments will be made on the illustrations first, followed by a general discussion of design considerations.

Figure 5.2 shows a preprinted form for bonus information. The actual size of the printing area is $10\frac{2}{3}$ by $6\frac{4}{5}$ inches. It is a two-part set of chemical reaction paper. The second copy is identical to the top copy. The style of the body of the form, with the alternating sets of plain and lined rows, is known as "flowline." The lines are dark gray, with the other preprinting in dark turquoise. It is an attractive form and fairly easy to handle because the pages are smaller than those of stock forms. The pages are, however, wider than they are deep. Even with the help of the flowlines, reading one line across could be difficult.

Figure 5.3 shows an entirely different type of preprinted form.

BONUS STATEMENT

F.C. 1541

NOTE:- WHEN TIME ALLOWED EQUALS TIME TAKEN AND NO QUANTITY GOOD IS SHOWN THE BONUS EARNED IS CARRIED FORWARD TO THE FOLLOWING WEEK

CLAIMS FOR ERRORS OR OMISSIONS MUST BE MADE TO THE WAGES OFFICE WITHIN TWO WEEKS FROM RECEIPT OF THIS STATEMENT.

CLOCK NO.	GRADE AND DEPT. WORKED	DEPT. AND REASON CODE	ORDER NUMBER	DRAWING NUMBER	OPN NO.	RATE	QUANTITY GOOD	MINS. ALLOWED	MINS. TAKEN	MINS. GAINED	% GAIN	TIME RECON.	WK. NO

HOOK LOCK® JAMSON IMAGON

50

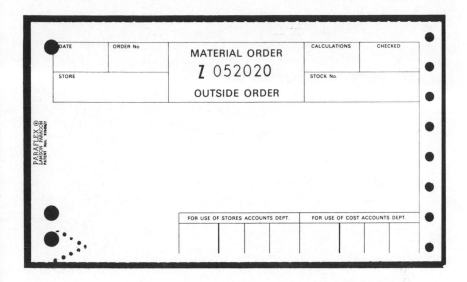

Fig. 5.3 Example of preprinted form: Material order (Courtesy Lamson Paragon)

This is an order form in three parts, with one-time carbon paper. The printing area is small, but still wider than it is long: 6⅔ by 4 inches. The headings, box lines, and comments are preprinted, as is the form number (top center). On all copies the date, order number, and store identification (upper left) are printed during the computer run, as are the stock number (upper right) and details of the items required (center). The top copy is white; this one stays in the company. There is space for handwritten comments and calculations by various departments. The second and third copies go to the supplier. The second one is pink; this is returned by the supplier with the materials. The third copy is yellow, on paper of heavier weight. It is kept by the supplier for his records. The strip of guide holes on the left can be detached, bringing with it both sheets of carbon paper in one operation. All three copies are prepunched in the left-hand margin for filing in a loose-leaf binder or post-hole ledger.

Of special note in Figure 5.3 is the fact that the form numbers are serial. On the top copy the six-digit number is red, but because it was printed after the sets were made up, it has come through onto the second and third parts in black. Adding a serial number is a separate print run requiring special equipment. It adds to the cost of the stationery, but also adds a measure of control. Each form can be accounted for, even spoiled ones, ensuring that none go astray.

DESIGN CRITERIA

A Starting Point

Designing good report layouts is really a specialist's job; the fact that it is left to systems analysts unexperienced in forms design accounts for many of the poorly designed reports in use. If there is an expert available within the company, on the staff of the data processing department or elsewhere, his services should be sought whenever possible. Failing this, the analyst will have to go ahead on his own; the notes provided here are intended as guidelines. Care and thoughtfulness in designing the reports, with careful testing of the trial designs before programming begins (discussed at the end of this chapter), can usually produce satisfactory results.

If at all possible, start with an existing report. Don't design a new report, redesign the old one. Users will be familiar with the data and the layout, thus shortening the familiarization period at implementation time. Furthermore, the design job will be very much easier because fewer decisions will be required. Starting with something is always better than starting with nothing.

Size and Shape

The size and shape of the form depend largely on whether stock paper or preprinted stationery will be used. Stock paper will be available in a limited number of sizes, perhaps only one. Preprinted forms can be any size and shape, limited only by the maximum and minimum dimensions required by the line printer. The major considerations are ease of use and the economics of high-speed line printers.

Information previously collected from the user department can provide an estimate of the number of lines of data that will occur on an average page. A "page" should correspond to a logical unit or logically connected groups of data. For example, a sales report may require information to be printed in the sequence of product number within product group. Do all the figures relating to one product form a unit equivalent to one page of printing? If not, one product group? If some such one-page group can be found, can it be arranged so that on 95 percent of the pages, all the information for the group will fit on one page? The objective is to minimize or eliminate those situations in which one full page plus only one or two lines on the next page are required. If this can be done, considerations of economics and of ease of use will both be met.

There is another area, however, where economics and convenience are usually in direct conflict. The mechanics of line printers require that for speed of printing, print lines should be wide and the paper should be wider than it is long. It takes virtually as long to print a line of 20 characters as it does to print one of 132 characters. This fact leads to attempts to cram as much data as possible onto one line. But the longer the lines and the less space there is between rows and columns, the more difficult it is to read and understand the material. Studies have shown that the ideal line length for human reading speed and comprehension is between 2 and $3\frac{1}{2}$ inches. Typical stock paper is about 16 inches wide. It is this characteristic of impact line printers that leads to so many poorly designed reports and complaints from those who have to use them. The systems analyst should always keep this problem in mind when deciding on paper size and shape, and try to find an acceptable compromise. What an acceptable compromise is will depend on installation standards, the user's previous experience, the speed of the line printer to be used, and the total configuration and throughput speed of the hardware. Suggestions for page layout in light of this problem will be given below.

General office procedure will affect the size and shape of the form, too. If it is to be filed, the page will have to be within the dimensions of the filing compartment, or else will have to be folded. If further data is to be added later on a typewriter, the characteristics of the machine must be known so that the width of the form will not be greater than that of the typewriter platen. If separated sheets are to be handled, square sheets are very inconvenient because they are difficult to arrange right side up in a pile. Very small and very large sizes, too, pose problems: Small ones are hard to arrange and get lost easily; large ones are difficult to handle and store.

The Use of Color

Like Model-T Fords, computer line printers can print in any color as long as it is black. There is no choice of color for data printed by computer. But choices are possible for the paper, the carbon paper, and for all data that is preprinted. The reasons for using color on continuous stationery depend on who will receive it and how it will be used. Color can increase ease of identification for sorting, distribution, and filing, make the data easier to read, highlight key fields, and greatly enhance aesthetic appeal. The major drawback is that colored paper and printing in color, especially when more than one colored ink is required, are more expensive than stock colors and black-on-white printing. Other minor disadvantages, depending on the application, could be that colors do not show up in photocopying, that a color-code system can be difficult to expand, that color dyes may reduce the value of the paper as pulp, and that some people are color blind.

To illustrate the last point, a color-coding system using pink for the accounts copy and pale green for the customer's copy is worse than useless if the clerk who is supposed to sort and distribute them cannot distinguish between the colors; red column headings for debit figures will be meaningless to a reader who sees red as black (a common form of color blindness). Possible confusion because of this can be avoided by not depending entirely on color coding for identification; the identification name or description should also be printed.

Some general rules of thumb for choice of colors are as follows:

1. If a color-coding system is already in use, do not change it.
2. Use pale colors for the paper and strong colors for the printing.
3. The most legible color combinations are black printing on yellow paper, green on white, red on white, and black on buff. Worst are green on red and red on green.
4. Use clear colors rather than muddy ones.
5. Fluorescent lighting changes some colors; test under actual conditions.
6. Reserve the use of red for its traditional warning: danger, fragile, urgent, overdue, secret, use special care.
7. Horizontal and vertical lines, when printed in color, should be slightly thicker than if they were black, for the same effect.

Typography

Preprinted forms allow choices in the style and weight of the type font used. The analyst should check on standard type fonts in use in the organization and follow past practice if at all possible. Important advantages of preprinted forms come into play here; UPPER and lower case, *italic* and **bold,** and different weights of type can be used to add emphasis, increase legibility, and save space on the form. As a general rule it is best not to mix more than three different combinations of weights and sizes of type on the same form and to keep the size of the type in proportion to the size of the page and the space around the printing. A giant title on a small sheet will look ridiculous; a tiny column heading over a wide column of figures will get lost. Consult with the stationery printer, and get proofs before finalizing the order.

Titles and Headings

Titles and headings, whether preprinted or printed by computer, require careful design. They should be brief, but informative and distinctive. The maximum number of characters possible for each heading will be governed by the number of character positions on that portion of the page, especially if they are printed by computer. The rule is to avoid abbreviations if possible, but this is rarely possible for column and row headings. If an abbreviation is essential, the user of the report should be asked for the standard or acceptable abbreviation, one that will be meaningful to him. Report codes or other coding systems that are part of standard practice are always acceptable, but they should also carry a descriptive, narrative title.

Headings should be distinct from the body of the data. This is easy to achieve if the headings are preprinted or if the data is entirely numeric. Other methods are underlining and extra spacing between headings and data.

Titles and headings should be repeated on every page of the report. Each title should include not only the descriptive name of the report, but two sets of dates. The first set indicates the period for which the data is valid. The second date is the day the report was actually printed. For example, "Quarterly Cash Flow Analysis, First Quarter 1975—April 4, 1975"; "Machine Utilization for Week of September 1–6, 1975; printed September 10."

In special circumstances titles and headings might be omitted altogether. This is possible either when the data is self-explanatory to the user, or when a special template is used, laid over the report, showing the headings. The two types of circumstances that make this necessary or desirable would be when considerable time and cost savings can be achieved by not printing the extra material, or when the data is secret and confidential. In the latter case the report template can be kept locked in someone's safe; without it the report would be meaningless to accidental browsers or determined spies. Because of the inconvenience, however, omitting titles and headings should be done only when essential, and only with the approval of the user.

Page Numbering

Page numbers are usually considered to be part of the heading of the report and may be printed on the same line as the first line of the heading. The conventional position for the page number is near the upper right-hand corner. All reports of more than one page should be numbered; this is a fairly simple programming problem. In addition, it is helpful to print "last page" on the last page of the report to indicate to the computer operators and data control staff that the last page or pages have not been lost.

Sometimes users may insist on numbering in the style of "page x of y," y being the total number of pages. If the total number of pages can vary, programming becomes somewhat more complicated because the number must be known before any printing begins. How this can be done depends on the required processing. If it is always the case that one master file record will produce one line of printing, some program previous to the print program can do a count of the master records and pass the information to the print program. It is then only necessary to divide by the number of lines per page, remembering to take into account summary pages and pages that will not contain all print lines. If some scheme such as this is not possible, the alternative is to format the report and write it out to tape or disk, counting the pages, then read that file back for printing. This can considerably increase the run time of the system, so the analyst should be sure that "page x of y" numbering is truly necessary before proceeding with the system design.

Sequence of the Data

The sequence of the data on the report page will probably be dictated by logical sequences inherent in the structure of the information, by the user's requirements, or by both. As examples of the logical sequence, detailed data is usually placed before summary figures; customer's name and address are placed before account details. For ease of use of the report, however, it might be better to print the summary lines first; or it might be more useful to show account balance first, followed by identification details. It is for purposes such as these that a careful investigation of the requirements for the output is necessary at an earlier stage in the project.

Other considerations for placement of data on the page are also related to the uses that will be made of the forms. If distribution information is needed—for example, department name and number—it should be placed near the top or highlighted so that it is visually easy to find. If pages are to be sorted by hand, or filed, the key information for these purposes should be similarly highlighted or placed in a corner—the upper right-hand corner is usually preferred.

Spacing of the Data

A key consideration for layout and spacing of the data on the page has already been mentioned several times. It is the need for long lines to take full advantage of the speed of the line printer, a requirement in direct conflict with ease of reading the information. The solution to the dilemma depends partly on whether the data is essentially narrative as opposed to columnar.

An example of a columnar-type report reduced in size can be seen in Figure 5.4. The difficulty of reading across a long line is even more evident when it is realized that the actual length of a line on this report as it comes from the computer is $12\frac{1}{2}$ inches. The problem is accentuated by the wide gaps between items on a line. The space between "region name" and "current balance," for example, could possibly be closed up. It would, of course, be necessary to know the lengths of the longest possible region name and the longest possible current balance. It is certainly true that the space between "zip code" and "notice sent" could be shortened. The saving grace of this design is the extra spacing between lines. Without it, the reader would find it impossible to read across one line without danger of losing his place. (It should also be noted that this example does not conform to recommendations for showing the date in the title). In spite of this criticism, however, this report is still better looking and easier to use than many others.

An alternative to the type of layout shown in the example would be to arrange the data in narrower lines, but print them two-up or three-up across the page. As was said earlier, the programming for this variation is not particularly complicated. Difficulties could arise if it were necessary to cut the pages vertically as well as horizontally after printing; in that case the extra cost of doing so might override considerations of ease of use. Also, although two-up design overcomes the objections to long lines of printing, it would be necessary for the user to become accustomed to the right-left sequence.

If the material to be printed is narrative, organized into sentences and paragraphs, three-up or four-up printing becomes a necessity. It has been proven that comprehension of written material drops when the reading speed is less than 150 words a minute. The absence of lower-case letters, and the poor print image given by a line printer,

```
IEF142I - STEP WAS EXECUTED - COND CODE 0000
IEF285I    DAN.LIB                                           PASSED
IEF285I    VOL SER NOS= OSWKO1.
IEF285I    SYS73129.T152312.RV000.DATEST.GOSET              PASSED
IEF285I    VOL SER NOS= OSWKO4.
IEF285I    SYS73129.T152312.SV000.DATEST.R0000209           SYSOUT
IEF285I    VOL SER NOS= OSWKO4.
IEF285I    SYS73129.T152312.SV000.DATEST.R000021C           DELETED
IEF285I    VOL SER NOS= OSWKO1.
IEF285I    SYS73129.T152312.RV000.DATEST.SORTDATA           DELETED
IEF285I    VOL SER NOS= OSWKO5.
IEF285I    SYS73129.T152312.SV000.DATEST.R0000211           DELETED
IEF285I    VOL SER NOS= OSWKO4.
IEF285I    SYS73129.T152312.SV000.DATEST.R0000212           DELETED
IEF285I    VOL SER NOS= OSWKO5.
IEF285I    SYS73129.T152312.RV000.DATEST.DAEDWK             DELETED
IEF285I    VOL SER NOS= OSWKO1.
IEF285I    SYS73129.T152312.SV000.DATEST.R0000213           .DELETEC
IEF285I    VOL SER NOS= SYSRES.
IEF285I    SYS73129.T152312.SV000.DATEST.R0000214           DELETED
IEF285I    VOL SER NOS= OSWKO1.
IEF285I    SYS73129.T152312.SV000.DATEST.R0000215           DELETED
IEF285I    VOL SER NCS= OSWKO4.
IEF285I    SYS73129.T152312.RV000.DATEST.S0000216           SYSIN
IEF285I    VOL SER NCS= OSWKO5.
IEF285I    SYS73129.T152312.RV000.DATEST.S0000216           DELETED
IEF285I    VOL SER NOS= OSWKO5.
IEF373I STEP /GO        / START  73129.1647
IEF374I STEP /GO        / STOP   73129.1648 CPU    OMIN 15.09SEC MAIN    40K LCS
IEF285I    DAN.LIB                                           KEPT
IEF285I    VOL SER NOS= OSWKO1.
IEF285I    SYS73129.T152312.RV000.DATEST.SORTPAR            DELETED
IEF285I    VOL SER NCS= OSWKO4.
IEF285I    SYS73129.T152312.RV000.DATEST.SRTCATA            DELETED
IEF285I    VOL SER NOS= SYSRES.
IEF285I    SYS73129.T152312.RV000.DATEST.GOSET              DELETED
IEF285I    VOL SER NOS= OSWKO4.
IEF375I JOB /DATEST   / START  73129.1633
IEF376I JOB /DATEST   / STOP   73129.1648 CPU    OMIN 57.22SEC
```

Fig. 5.4 Example of report: Demand deposit accounts (Courtesy Program Products, Inc.)

lower reading speed anyway. If a very long line length is added, comprehension suffers markedly. If narrower forms cannot be used, the alternative is a printout in narrower columns, giving the appearance of a newspaper. Programming does become more complicated in this case. It is necessary to lay out the entire page in memory before printing of the first line can begin. Another possible difficulty is that a higher proportion of the number of available print positions will be wasted when there is not enough space for the next word on the line, requiring extra blanks to be left at the end of the line. Because there are more lines, this will happen more often. (Right justification of print lines should not be attempted. Word division under program control is a specialist's area and very difficult to achieve with any degree of success. Furthermore, computer printers do not have variable spacing).

Output Editing

Commercial programming languages offer powerful output editing features. Some examples are suppression of left-hand zeros; variable placing of punctuation such as dollar signs, commas, and decimal points; debit signs for negative amounts; and automatic addition of special characters such a @, *, etc. The possibilities vary depending on the programming language to be used. The systems analyst should study the programming manual to see what options are available before specifying the report layout. In some cases it will be desirable to explain the choices to the user for his decision on the most useful features.

DESIGN CHECKOUT

Before finalizing the report specifications, the systems analyst should "test" his designs by showing them to the people who will be concerned in developing the system and using the reports. This testing is, of course, preliminary to program and systems testing. Its objective is to find and correct any deficiencies in the content and design of the reports, and to do this *before* programming begins. A print program that formats and writes several complicated reports from several sets of files is a large one. Changing the report contents and layout after programming has begun can be very expensive. Any extra time used earlier to improve the reports will be well spent.

Design checkout begins with the designer himself, who should review the report layouts and specifications against the users' requirements and against installation standards for design and documentation. (It should be mentioned in passing that documentation of report layouts and output procedures is not within the scope of this chapter; those interested will find sample standards in Appendix C.)

Following his own review, the designer can next consult with representatives from the following departments: programming, operations, data control, and user.

The programming review is particularly important if the designer himself is not experienced in the programming language to be used. There are always "tricks of the trade" that will not be found in any programming manual but that might have an influence on the output design. The programmer who is consulted may be able to suggest minor changes in design for major improvements in ease and speed of programming, debugging, or running time. He may be able to point out editing facilities that could be used; or he may be able to suggest improvements in the documentation for easier understanding by programmers and operators.

The operations department will be looking at the output design from the point of view of ease of setup, running, and takedown. Frequent changes of paper for the printer, for example, are undesirable because they are time consuming. An experienced operator may be able to spot some minor design change that would reduce the number of paper changes required. He will also be familiar with the actual capabilities of the installation's printer. He may be able to point out improvements in the report layout or the preprinted portion of the stationery that will make alignment of the forms in the printer easier and more accurate. He may also have suggestions for increasing the degree of control over prenumbered forms such as checks and invoices.

The data control people are interested in the forms handling procedures after the output has left the computer room. These can include bursting, decollating, folding, binding, and distribution. They can comment on the ease with which these tasks can be accomplished. A more detailed discussion of ancillary procedures will be found in Chapter 8.

The review by the user is the most important one. He will be most interested in the content and ease of use of the reports. The designer, therefore, should not present him with layouts documented on the forms used for programming; a multitude of little boxes filled with X's, 9's, and mysterious symbols is confusing even to users who have seen them before, and cannot give a correct impression of how the report will finally look. Instead, mock-ups of the report, looking as much like the real thing as possible, can be used. If preprinted forms are not available, a realistic substitute is the preliminary artwork or proofs. Dummy report samples are easy to produce on the computer, although it may be necessary to use stock paper rather than preprinted forms at this stage. A card-to-printer program is simple to write, although it is more than likely that the installation already has a utility program that will do this. Failing an actual computer-produced report, one can be done on a typewriter, being sure that only upper-case characters are used. The content of each dummy report should be realistic. An order for nine dozen cases of dehydrated water to be delivered to Buckingham Palace will not amuse a senior manager. Use actual data, and be sure that the totals balance.

It is here that the user has his last opportunity for changes before programming begins. Systems analysts who complain that the users are always changing their minds and causing delays in the project will find that changes now, before programming, are much better than changes later. The user needs time to study the mock-ups, and he should be questioned carefully about each layout. Does it contain the information he needs in the most useful format? Also, does he understand the procedures for production and distribution? Will the data reach him in time? Will it be up-to-date enough for effective use?

If the systems designer has gone about his task of specifying these reports in an intelligent and careful manner, and followed the suggestions given here for checkout of the design, he can now proceed to incorporate any changes that were recommended. He now documents his work for handover to the programming section.

SUMMARY

This chapter has covered the design of reports to be produced on a high-speed computer line printer, taking into consideration the restrictions imposed by the device. It has not considered other methods of output that attempt to overcome these disadvantages; computer output microfilm is discussed in Chapter 9, and graphic output—both from the line printer and from plotters—is covered in Part Four. The content has also been restricted to batch, as opposed to on-line output, which is covered in Part Three. Finally, no mention has yet been made of error reports and designing error correction and resubmission procedures; this will be found in the next chapter.

CHAPTER 6

Error and Control Reports and Procedures

The design of error detection and correction procedures is closely linked with the design of the input subsystem, particularly the input edit programs. Most of the errors eventually shown on error reports or exception reports will have originated in the input stream. Some incorrect data will have been wrong when it was initially entered on source documents, other errors will have been made in the keying operation, and some may have arisen as the data was read into the first computer program. A large part of the design effort for input procedures has to be devoted to preventing errors, and to detecting and correcting them if they cannot be prevented. It is at this point that an input problem changes to one of output. The errors must be reported, corrected, and then the corrections reinput into the system. It is thus obvious that output cannot be discussed in isolation from input design. Although input design is the subject of another book, this chapter must begin with a summary of input control procedures.

INPUT CONTROLS

There are two major categories of erroneous input data: *accidentally* corrupted data and *deliberately* corrupted data. The computer system must include controls to prevent, detect, and correct both types. Accidental errors are usually caused by humans in data handling and transcription, although misreads by computer equipment also contribute. Deliberate corruption of data may take place as a result of attempts to defraud the company through the computer system, or as a means of revenge for some wrong, imagined or real. Most of the checks and controls outlined below are prevention and detection measures against both categories of bad input.

Manual Checking

Possibilities for human checking of input data begin where the data originate, which is usually in one of the user departments. The scope of such checking can vary from a quick visual scan of completed source documents to a thorough double check of every item entered.

Keying Verification

Any data that is keyed, whether for punched cards, paper tape, magnetic tape, or a key-to-disk input system, can be double-checked by a rekeying operation called "verification." Eighty percent of keying errors are conscious; that is, the operator knows at once that the wrong character has been entered. With some types of input it is possible to correct the character at once; with other types, the entire record must be rekeyed from the beginning. Unconscious keying errors can be found and corrected by verification.

Batching

Most high-volume input is amenable to batch controls of some kind. The mechanics are not complicated. As the input is originated—say, written onto source documents—the documents are accumulated into groups or batches and counted. A control slip is attached to each batch showing the number of documents in it. In the simplest example, one punched card is created for each document. The cards are also held in batches and counted, with a control card added to the front containing the batch number and the number of cards. Other data can be added, for example, the date, counts of the numbers of different types of transactions in the batch, control totals, and hash totals. The first program in the computer subsystem counts the cards as they are read and checks the batch against the information in the control card. Any discrepancy can cause the rejection of one or more cards or of the entire batch. Variations in batch procedures depend on the application, the degree of control required, the input method, and the ingenuity of the systems designer.

Check Digits

A check digit is a number added to the end of the existing field to ensure that each time the field is copied, no errors have occurred. The check digit is derived by applying some arithmetic formula to the original number, and after the number has been copied or read by computer equipment, the same arithmetic process is applied in reverse, as it were; the same check digit should result each time if no error has been made.

The most popular check digit method multiplies each digit in the original field by a predetermined number (the weights), sums the results, and divides the sum by another number (the modulus) which is usually a prime number. The weights are 2 3 4 5 6 . . . and the modulus is 11, although other systems can be used. For a code of 64175, finding the check digit would be done as follows:

1. Multiply by the weights:
$$6 \times 6 = 36$$
$$4 \times 5 = 20$$
$$1 \times 4 = 4$$
$$7 \times 3 = 21$$
$$5 \times 2 = 10$$

2. Sum the products:
$$36 + 20 + 4 + 21 + 10 = 91$$

3. Divide by the modulus 11:

$$
\begin{array}{r}
8 \\
11\overline{)91} \\
\underline{88} \\
3
\end{array}
$$

4. Find the complement of the remainder 3 to the modulus 11:

$$
\begin{array}{r}
11 \\
\underline{3} \\
8
\end{array}
$$

5. The check digit is 8.

The number 8 is then added to the original number, thus 64175–8. After any copying operation, the arithmetic above is repeated, this time adding the check digit into the sum of the products. When the sum is divided by 11, the remainder should always be zero. If it is not, an error has been made in copying the number (or, obviously, in copying the check digit).

The system described will detect 98.7 percent of all copying errors. A higher prime number for the modulus, 37, for example, will detect 99.9 percent of errors.

Doing this arithmetic by hand would obviously be very tedious and error prone. Other methods must therefore be used. Among the most popular are via a "black box" attached to the keypunch machine, where the number is buffered and the check digit calculated before punching the card or paper tape takes place; or by computer, either in a data entry system or in the main frame computer during the edit program.

It is not economic to attach a check digit to every field going through the computer system. Whether or not to use one depends on the result of a cost benefit analysis—that is, the cost of undetected errors entering the system versus the cost of using check digits—against the benefit of being assured of a high level of accuracy. The analysis can be made by asking, first, whether there is an easier way of catching errors, and if there is not, what the effects of undetected errors would be. Processing an incorrect product number and sending the wrong product to a customer would not be as serious as processing an incorrect customer number and sending an entire order to the wrong place. Or, supplying the wrong medication would be very bad, but possibly not as bad as operating on the wrong patient. The systems analyst must work with the user to determine the seriousness of possible errors, and then make a decision about the amount of time and effort that should be invested to prevent them.

AUDIT TRAILS

An audit trail is a tracing procedure to follow the path of any individual transaction through the computer system. An example of an audit trail for an order-processing and invoicing system is shown in Figure 6.1. All the documents and reports on the right-hand side of the flowchart constitute the audit trail. For each order processed by the system, the following documentation will exist:

1. Order details from customer (the original source document)
2. Batch of punched cards representing order
3. Control listing of punched cards representing order
4. Edit report showing whether entire order was accepted as correct

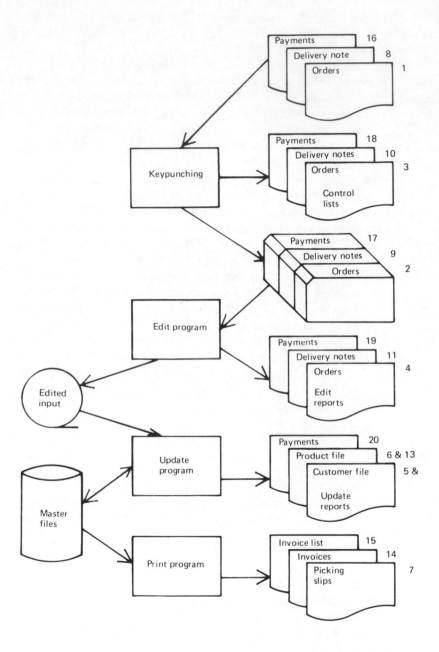

Fig. 6.1 Example of an audit trail

66

5. Update report showing order data entered onto customer's master record
6. Update report showing order data entered onto product master record
7. Packing slip used by warehouse to assemble order
8. Delivery note signed by customer indicating acceptance of order
9. Batch of punched cards representing delivery note
10. Control listing of punched cards representing delivery note
11. Edit report showing whether entire delivery note was accepted as correct
12. Update report showing delivery data entered onto customer's master record
13. Update report showing any adjustments to product master file (for example, if an item in the order was not accepted by the customer)
14. Copy of invoice sent to customer
15. Control listing showing invoice details
16. Payment details from accounts department (who will also have a copy of the bank deposit slip)
17. Punched cards showing payment details
18. Control listing showing payment details
19. Edit report showing whether payment details accepted as correct
20. Update report showing payment details entered onto customer's master record

There are thus 20 different sets of documents showing the progression of one order through the system. If any exception processing took place—for example, if the customer returned goods after an invoice was issued—there could be many more. Two of these, the original order from the customer and the payments list from the accounts department, are source documents; two are sets of punched cards; the remaining 16 documents are output generated by the computer system. There is a further source of information available to anyone wishing to double-check: a listing of the master files themselves.

It must be pointed out here that the level of control supplied by the audit trail in this example is excessive for this type of system. The example is given to illustrate what *can* be done, not necessarily what *should* be done. The level of detail required for an audit trail should be specified by the accountants in the organization, and will depend not only on the type of system but on the accounting practices employed. The high level of control shown in this example might, however, be used during systems testing and the first operating cycles of a new system as an aid to tracing and correcting bugs. It could then be reduced. The items most likely to be eliminated would be steps 3, 5, 6, 10, 12, 13, and 20, that is, copies of information already available at other places in the system.

There are two main uses of an audit trail. The first is to enable company management, especially the accountants and auditors, to follow transactions through the system step by step. They can thus verify that the record-keeping procedures are accurate and that the system is adequately protected against fraud. If a fraud is suspected, the audit trail can supply the necessary verification.

The second purpose of the audit trail is to make finding and correcting errors as easy as possible, whether the errors are previously undetected bugs in the programming or incorrect input. By following the audit trail backward from the point where the error was first detected, it is possible to find where it originated. Corrected data can then be resubmitted to the system. If appropriate, steps can be taken to correct the bug or to improve input procedures to prevent the error happening again.

CONTROL REPORTS

A control report, or control listing, is a printout showing details of the processing that has been done. The level of detail given should be sufficient to allow an independent assessment to be made of the completeness and accuracy of the processing. There are two broad categories of control reports. One type provides information for use by the data processing department in checking on the correct functioning of the system. The other is for the user department, to allow them to check on the content of the files and the accuracy of the record keeping.

Control reports for use within data processing are concerned not so much with the content of the master files as with the technical accuracy of the processing. For example, an update control report might show numbers of records processed, as follows:

Number of records on old master file	12,397
Number of new records created	122
Number of records deleted	32
Number of records on new master file	12,487

Obviously, the number of old records plus the new ones created minus the number deleted should equal the number of records on the new master file. If it does not, this is a clear danger signal that something has gone wrong in the processing (or in the control routine). This type of control report can be expanded further, depending on the details of the processing. The number of blocks can be counted, as well as the number of records; counts of the different types of transactions read in and processed can be made and related to the master records they were processed against. Also, the control report from this run can be checked against the previous one; in the example above, "Number of records on new master file" should have been 12,397 on the previous report.

The scope of systems control reports is wide. What types are produced for any particular system will depend on the type of application, the installation's standards, the requirements of the auditors, and previous experience within the installation. The number of reports to have, and their content, should be decided on in consultation with the users and with data processing management, as well as the company accountants and auditors. If standards have already been established, the problem is only one of interpreting and applying them.

User control reports, those supplying details of the content of the processing, deserve even more attention. They are particularly important for any accounting system or any system processing details of cash or its equivalent in credit or goods.

Let us take an example from the system outlined in Figure 6.1. Each customer's record contains a field showing balance outstanding, that is, what he owes the company. In each run this is updated by adding in the total value of any new orders (debits) and subtracting any payments made (credits). There are other possible transactions, for example, returns and discounts. This is actually a simple sales ledger system. If all the outstanding balances are added together during the run, the total will show how much money is owed to the company. This field can be kept in a control record at the end of the file. During the update, the processing for each master record proceeds as described above. At the same time, running totals are kept of the credits, the debits, and the new balances outstanding. At the end of the run, the control record is read in. The old balances oustanding field is updated by adding in the total debits and subtracting the total credits. The result should equal the control total of balances built up during processing. If it does not, this is an immediate warning that some tampering with the files has occurred or that there is a bug somewhere in the system.

The examples given so far have been for balancing through a file. The control report produced at the end of the run would be small, perhaps only one page. More detailed control listings can be printed, showing individual record details. In an update, for example, a detailed control listing would show the old master record before it was updated, details of all transactions processed against it, and the new master record after processing. This level of detail would obviously require a very long print run and is not suitable for every update. It might, however, be done in the following situations:

1. During systems testing
2. During parallel running
3. Once a year, for auditor's use
4. When requested by auditors or accountants
5. For selected records, on request
6. For randomly selected records

There is also another type of control report, one that signals a possible error situation rather than an absolute one. Details are printed out only when certain predetermined situations exist. There are many possible examples; three will be given. The first is common practice for payroll systems. Control records are kept with totals from the last payroll and compared with totals from this one. Percentage differences, such as total overtime worked 10 percent more than last week or total payroll 8 percent more than last week, would cause a warning report to be printed. In the second example, from the sales ledger system outlined earlier, a warning report could be printed when the total returned goods exceeded the annual average by $1000 or more. The third example has to do with credit control, in which details of the record of any customer whose credit limit has been raised by more than 50 percent in the last three months are printed for human inspection.

As can be seen, there are many ways to provide control information. Merely printing it out, however, is of little value if the reports are not read and acted on. When designing this part of the computer system, procedures for distribution and use of the reports must also be planned. Distributing the right reports to the right people is still not enough; the reports must be read and acted on in time to prevent disasters. Knowing that double refunds have been erroneously issued to every customer is not particularly helpful two weeks after the event; knowing that the company's bank account has been cleaned out by embezzlers is of little use after the criminals have fled the country.

The user must understand the purpose of the control reports, be able to interpret their contents, and be consulted when production and distribution procedures are designed. It is the responsibility of the systems analyst to see to it that this takes place.

THE EDIT PROGRAM

So far we have dealt with system and user control reports for verification of the accuracy of processing; but the most rigidly controlled processing is of little avail if the data being processed is inaccurate. This chapter began with descriptions of some of the input controls that can be applied before the data reach the computer subsystem. The first computer program is usually an input edit program, and of particular concern here is the edit report that is output from it. The content and layout of that report are often the most difficult design decisions to be made concerning the whole system, and the success of the system can depend on them.

The design philosophy of the edit program itself, reflected in the output report, should be that all errors will be found and reported. Although this ideal cannot always be reached, either because one error masks others or because certain control information is not available to the edit program, it should be kept in mind during specifications of the checks to be made.

Types of Checking

The types of checks that can be performed by the edit program are summarized below.

1. Batch controls (as described above)
2. Control totals (as described above)
3. Check digit calculations (as described above)
4. Presence checks (to be sure that required fields exist)
5. Cross-reference presence checks (For example, if the transaction code is B, the next field must be five alphabetic characters)
6. Format checks for leading zeroes, blanks, numerics, alphabetics, and special characters
7. Range checks for upper and lower values
8. Reasonableness checks (also based on upper and lower values but not necessarily signaling a failure)

9. Sequence checks if input transactions are required in a preset
sequence
10. Master reference checks for valid key fields (if possible)

Contents of the Error Report

The output report from the edit program must not only contain
information about rejected or suspect input but must also provide sufficient detail for identification and correction of the data. For this
reason it is useful to classify errors into three groups: those involving
(or suspected of involving) an entire batch, those involving two or
more records in a batch (where the records are logically related), and
those involving only one record, whether only one field or several are
suspect. As a general rule identification is relatively more easy for a
batch than for an individual item but correction is relatively more
difficult. The goal is to provide adequate information for both purposes.

Batch errors include incorrect or missing batch header records,
unreconcilable control totals, and incorrect batch counts. They usually
require rejection of the entire batch. In line with the goal of detecting
every error, however, if it is possible to do so, individual records in
the batch should be edited and errors reported even though none of
the transactions will, in fact, be passed for processing. It may be desirable to list every record in the batch, whether it is correct or not;
this is especially true if the error involves the batch header record. In
any case, full details of the expected values and the actual values
should be given, as well as a report that the batch has been rejected.

Where two or more logically related records in the batch are rejected, each must be listed. It is preferable to show them in the sequence in which they were read; otherwise errors involving wrong
sequences may not be evident. The batch they came from and, if possible, their relative positions in the batch should be reported, along
with the reason for rejection. As before, further editing of individual
fields should be done even though the entire record is rejected. In cases
of this kind it is usually necessary to list every record in the batch,
even correct ones, to provide sufficient information for locating and
correcting the records in error.

Rejects involving only one record do not usually require listing
of the entire batch. It is necessary, however, to identify the batch and
the relative position of the rejected record in the batch. Then the
record itself must be clearly identified by the transaction code and key
fields, if possible. There is always a dilemma as to whether to print an
exact image of the record as it was received or to explode and identify

the fields for easier reading. On the one hand, 80 characters without spacing or punctuation marks are difficult to read and interpret; on the other hand, exploded and edited fields may mask the errors that exist. An acceptable compromise is usually to do both, clearly specifying which is which. For the unedited version, the field or fields in question can be highlighted by printing asterisks or other special characters under them.

It is then necessary to give as much detail as possible about the suspected error. The actual value and the expected value should be printed along with a description of the error. A narrative description is always preferable to a code number, provided that the narrative can be sufficiently detailed to say all there is to say. Some narratives would have to be quite long-winded to do this, however. Abbreviations can be more confusing than code numbers. The best compromise is to use codes as necessary, and then print the full table of codes and their associated narrative descriptions as a separate page of the edit report. This has several advantages over listing them in a reference manual, including the possibility of a reference manual getting lost and the fact that the codes can be changed by changing only the program and not the manual.

Layout of the Report

As with other batch reports the design choices involve economic use of paper and printer time balanced against ease of use and readability of the report. Many of the comments and guidelines given in the last chapter for design of the report format apply here as well. Efficient use of the hardware may more often come second, however, both because the volume of printing is apt to be lower and because legibility of the report can have a significant effect on the speed with which errors can be corrected and system processing brought up-to-date. Being able to continue processing with corrected data can outweigh any minor considerations of paper or computer time usage.

The sequence of the data on the report must be the same as that in which the data was read into the edit program. It may be tempting to sort the error records first so that they can be listed by transaction type, but this can make identification and location of the incorrect records difficult, if not impossible. Further, this may mask some types of errors. If it is desirable to try to correct all of one type of transaction at a time, before going on to other types, almost the same effect can be achieved by putting the transaction code in a prominent position, perhaps set out in the extreme left-hand or right-hand print positions.

Unless batches are very small, it is usually best to start reporting each batch on a new page, clearly identifying the batch at the top of the page. Also it is advisable to provide plenty of space between individual items, including room for handwritten notes if necessary. For ease of identification of errors, the best layout for individual print lines is to have one print line correspond to one record. If the maximum input record size is greater than the length of the print line, this will require going to a second line to finish the record. If that is absolutely unavoidable, it is preferable to break the new line at a break between fields, rather than splitting one field between two lines. If there is room, the code or error description is placed at the right, adjacent to the record image; if not it is placed underneath, with sufficient space to indicate clearly which narratives go with which record images.

The last page or pages of the error report should contain summary and control totals. There are two sets of these. The first is batch control information that is printed regardless of whether any errors were found. The second is the subtotals of the numbers of errors found, by type. This summary has two uses: first, to enable the person correcting the data to double-check that he has not omitted anything; second, to give statistics on the frequencies of different types of errors. These figures will indicate where extra training, rewriting of instruction manuals, redesign of input forms, and so on, can be best applied to reduce the numbers of input errors to the unavoidable minimum.

A summary of the guidelines for design of the error report is given in Figure 6.2.

Use same sequence as input.

Start each batch on a new page.

Print exact record image; if necessary, print exploded and edited image
as well.

Identify the batch.

Identify the record and its position in the batch.

If necessary for clear identification, list all records in the batch.

Clearly identify the error, using narrative description if possible.

If error codes must be used, print a table of the codes and their meanings
with each report.

Show all errors in each record.

Summarize types of errors.

Fig. 6.2   Guidelines for designing input error reports

REINPUT OF CORRECTED DATA

The exception or error report will show both absolute failures in which the transaction has not been passed on for further processing, and suspect or flagged items, in which processing is continuing.

For the second type, if it is in fact found to be correct, no action need be taken. If it is not correct, reinput of the record is necessary in order to correct files that the data has been applied to, and some additional action may be necessary to intercept the error before it leaves the system. For example, let us suppose that one of the range checks performed by the edit program was on the quantity ordered field. It is unusual enough to warrant a warning if Customer A has ordered 200 tractors when the average order is one. If a double check shows that A really does want 200, no further action is required. But if there has been an error and only one tractor is required, two things must be done. First, the documentation produced by the system must be intercepted and corrected by hand before it leaves the computer area for handling; second, a transaction must be reinput to correct all master files that have been updated with the wrong data.

When an item has been absolutely rejected, the time span for correction and resubmission depends on the system and its processing cycle. Some systems, especially those dealing with accounting data, require that all input be correct and balanced before processing can continue. This may mean several cycles of edit, report, correct, and reinput before all data is correct.

There are two methods of getting corrected input back into the system. The first requires that each corrected record be rekeyed and new input records created. This method is fairly straightforward, but may require a heavy keying load and consequent loss of time before processing can continue. The other method uses a separate magnetic tape or disk file to hold images of the rejected records until corrections are received. If only one field was in error, only that field (with an identifying code) need be rekeyed. When it is received by the edit program, the original erroneous record is retrieved and updated with the corrected field or fields.

One example of this method is shown in Figure 6.3. Note that here the corrected records are edited again, because it is possible that errors have been repeated or that the corrected field now allows identification of errors that were masked before. Also note that each day's rejects are added onto the previous day's reject file (when there is one). It is usually *not* advisable to create a new file for each edit run or one

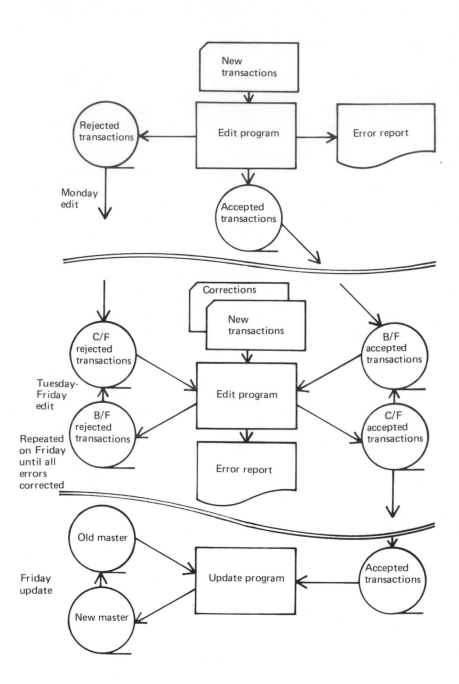

Fig. 6.3 Example of error reinput cycle

for each type of transaction. Instead, the rejects can be added onto the previous file. This will require that each rejected record be identified by batch and date. The illustration shows tape files that are reread by the edit program for update each day. By Friday, Monday's transactions will have been read and rewritten at least five times. A better method would be to add the new transactions (accepted or rejected) onto the end of the file each day. Alternatively, disk can be used; and other variations are also possible. For example, all corrections can be held and processed once, just before the update.

The advantages of keeping rejected records on file include not only a possible reduction of the rekeying load, but also a method of double-checking that all rejected records have been corrected. The edit program can add the date to the rejected record image, later checking that no rejects older than a predetermined age are still on the file.

SUMMARY

The design of error and control reports and procedures is an important part of the total design process. Consultation with the users and with company auditors when planning this part of the system will help the designer to ensure that the level of control provided is correct and that the reports and procedures are clear, easy to follow, and will fit the time scale required for processing. After the system is implemented, he should follow up to check that the error rate is an acceptable one and to see whether any part of the system could be improved.

CHAPTER 7

Multicopy Production

Many applications require more copies of the output than can be produced on the line printer in one run. In some cases this is a regular, predictable demand; in others, the need for extra copies arises only occasionally, or becomes known only after the computer run is finished. There are some situations in which the quality of the line printer carbon copies is not acceptable and every recipient needs a "top" copy. Each of these circumstances calls for some method of making additional copies of the output from the initial printout.

A typical example of the need for multiple copies is the company's catalog or price list. The information must be published at regular intervals and each user must have an up-to-date copy quickly. The same criteria apply to credit control applications, where the latest data must be in the hands of sales staff as soon as possible. Other examples are stock lists, directories, quotations for customers, sales reports, financial reports and statistical summaries for large meetings, and abstracts of data in information retrieval systems. All possess the characteristics of being information processed by computer, updated regularly, and needed for use by relatively large numbers of people within a tight distribution schedule.

Using the computer to make the extra copies is like using a sledgehammer to crack a nut. There are only a handful of situations in which it could possibly be justified. One is when additional copies are needed urgently and there is no faster method of obtaining them. It is difficult to imagine circumstances in which this could happen, but it might. Another example would be of the first output being inadvertently destroyed; if this happens more than very rarely, there are serious problems of management control. There is another situation, however, that is of a different nature; it arises when the forms are narrow enough to permit duplicates to be printed two-up or three-up across the paper and separated later. The line printer can make five or six legible copies, so two-up printing will give ten or twelve. Most applications requiring multicopy production, however, call for some other solution. There are 20 or 30 different methods of producing multiple copies, some of which are suitable for computer-produced printout. An examination of these methods shows about half a dozen from which a solution to almost any multicopy problem can emerge. They are photocopying (Xeroxing), dye-line duplicating, spirit duplicating, offset litho, and microfilm. A possible addition to that list could be automatic photocomposition or phototypesetting, which will be discussed later.

In this chapter each of the copying methods above will be discussed. A brief description of the process is followed by comments on advantages and drawbacks for various uses, and considerations for acquiring the equipment and implementing the procedures needed. Figure 7.1 gives a comparative summary of the methods discussed in terms of

Method	Max. Number of Copies from One Master	Useful Range
Computer printer	6	1–5
Photocopy	No limit	1–10
Dye line	40	5–15
Spirit duplicator	250	10–20
Offset litho		
paper plate	1000	20–50
metal plate	50,000	Up to 40,000
photographic plate	No limit	40,000–100,000
Microfilm	No limit	1–200

Fig. 7.1   Comparison of copying methods

the practical number of copies obtained. Comments will also be made about other factors that need to be considered when choosing the copying method.

PHOTOCOPY

To most people "photocopy" means Xerox, but it must be pointed out that strictly speaking photocopying is any duplicating process that uses a light source, and as such would include dye-line printing and several other techniques. It will be taken to mean only a xerographic process here, however.

The mechanics and chemistry of xerography were explained in Chapter 4. Most people who work in an office know how to operate the equipment and are familiar with the level of quality of the copies produced. In fact, its ease of operation is so great that overenthusiastic use makes it a very expensive toy in some offices. A mystique has grown up around Xerox machines to the extent that some executives unconsciously prefer a photocopy because it carries more cachet and more authenticity than the original.

Photocopying is the method of choice for producing a small number of copies on an irregular basis, provided the model used will accept full-sized continuous stationery sheets. Copying half of a sheet at a time and pasting the halves together is too slow and expensive to use as a regular procedure, and it is messy. Furthermore, the machine does need to be maintained and adjusted regularly, and amateur operation can produce copies of very poor quality.

There is a Xerox model that is of particular interest to data processing. It is especially designed to accept large computer printout sheets and will reduce them in size while copying. It is also possible to add a template containing headings and titles, so that these need not be printed by the computer. The whole process is automatic and will burst the forms after copying and then collate them. Cost savings for a dedicated machine appear only when the volume of work is high. Some installations using this method produce all computer reports on one-part standard stock paper, running off the necessary copies on the Xerox. Savings occur for various reasons in several areas, including

1. Ordering one-part stock paper in bulk
2. Fewer paper changes in the computer room
3. Faster printing because headings need not be printed
4. More characters per line because decimal points, and so on, can be added from the template
5. Demands for extra copies later mean only copying the master
6. Reduced size of paper cuts postage and distribution costs

In addition, everyone gets a "top" copy. Drawbacks are the relatively high cost and the need for heavy use to justify the cost. The process is available on a service bureau basis from printing bureaus.

DYE-LINE PROCESS

The dye-line or diazo duplicating process requires that the master be printed on special translucent paper, which can be obtained as continuous forms for computer production. Copies are made onto paper coated with an emulsion. Ultraviolet light passes through the master, burning away the emulsion on the copy everywhere except where the light is blocked by printing. The copy is then developed and fixed with an ammonia gas developer or by heat.

Up to 750 copies per hour can be made. The process is inexpensive when used for copies in the range of 5 to 15 per master. The quality of the copies is reasonably good. It is most suitable for relatively low volumes of work.

SPIRIT DUPLICATOR

Spirit duplication also requires that the master be produced on special paper. In this case the master is backed with hectographic carbon paper placed so that the carbon coating faces the back of the master sheet. Printing thus causes the carbon to adhere to the back in a mirror image. The copying uses a rotary press with the master fixed to a drum. The copy paper is dampened with spirit so that when it is pressed against the master, the spirit causes a small portion of hectographic carbon to adhere, giving an image of the printed material.

Up to 250 copies can be obtained from one master at rates of up to 30 per minute. Spirit duplication competes with dye-line copying for the smaller copying jobs, but it has one major advantage: It is possible to select only portions of the master to be printed on any one copy. Thus for printing customer's orders, for example, picking data can be shown only on the warehouse copy and credit details only on the account's copy, neither column appearing on the customer's copy.

OFFSET LITHOGRAPHY

Being able to produce offset-litho masters from the computer printer for copying runs of between 20 and 1000 copies makes offset lithography a method of prime consideration in many applications. To start the discussion it is necessary to define the terms "litho" and "offset."

Lithographic Process.   The lithographic process is an old one, the first printing being done from a stone, hence the name. The image to be printed was drawn on the stone in reverse image using a greasy substance. The stone was then wet with water, and ink was then applied by running an inked roller over the surface. The ink was also greasy and therefore was repelled by the water and clung only to the greased area. Copies could then be taken by pressing a sheet of paper onto the stone. Nowadays, the master plate can be made of paper, metal, or photographic film.

Offset Printing.   "Offset" refers to the mechanical process of doing the printing. The master plate is fixed in place. A roller, carrying water, is passed over it. Printed portions of the plate reject the water, which thus adheres only to blank areas. A second roller, carrying ink, is then passed over the plate, the ink adhering only to the dry areas. Then the printing roller (the blanket) is passed over the plate and picks up the ink; in other words the impression to be printed is offset onto the blanket. The blanket is then rolled over the copy paper, leaving the ink, and the copy is ejected into a stacker or tray. It can thus be seen that the master plate should be prepared in positive, rather than mirror image; the printing is reversed to mirror image onto the blanket and back again onto the copy sheet.

Many large suppliers of continuous forms for computer printers stock plain litho masters, or preprinted ones can be ordered. An example of a preprinted offset-litho master is shown in Figure 7.2. It is used to prepare the price catalogs for a large electronics manufacturer. (The preprinted headings are deliberately cryptic because the catalog is not intended to be seen by the general public.) An example of the printed page is shown in Figure 7.3. Note that very accurate registration of the printing is needed for the narrow columns, which is not difficult to accomplish on an offset-litho machine. The entire catalog contains some 180 pages bound into cardboard covers by gumming. It is updated once a quarter for distribution to more than 250 service centers and retailers around the country.

These paper plates are inexpensive and easy to obtain. They can be prepared at line printer speeds, the only extra work being a change of the ribbon in the printer before the run is started. The only handling required is after the run is bursting, and the plates are then ready for the offset machine. Up to 1000 good-quality copies can be obtained from one master plate. Paper plates can also be prepared by photographing ordinary computer printout, by using a typewriter or Varityper with a special ribbon, or by hand drawing with a special pen or pencil.

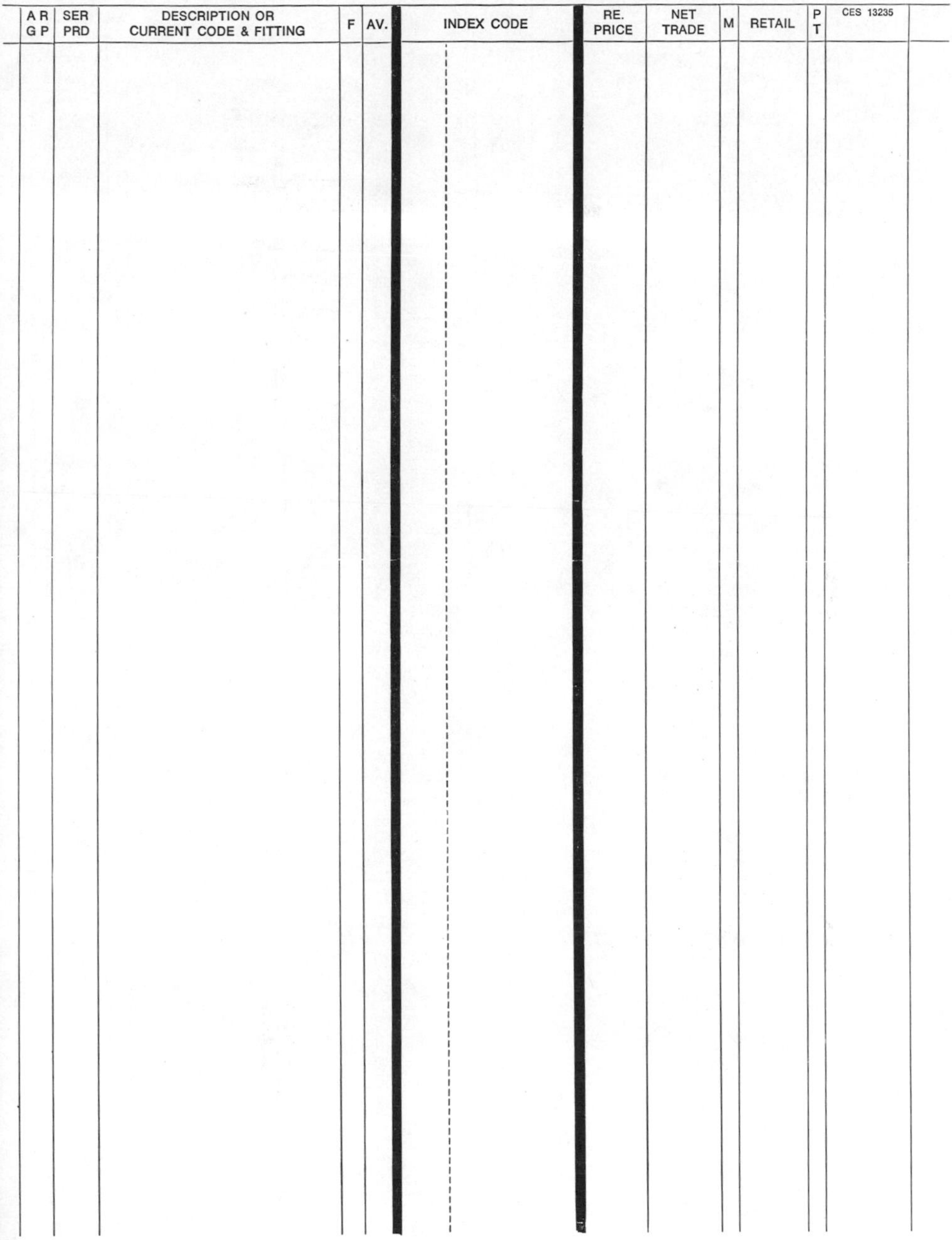

A R G P	SER PRD	DESCRIPTION OR CURRENT CODE & FITTING	F	AV.	INDEX CODE	RE. PRICE	NET TRADE	M	RETAIL	P T	CES 13235	

Fig. 7.2   Offset-litho plate

83

C C	A R G P	SER PRD	DESCRIPTION OR CURRENT CODE & FITTING	F	AV.	INDEX CODE	RE. PRICE	NET TRADE	M	RETAIL	P T
1	02	81	TUNER UNIT UHF	*		21047021			3	11.25	A
1	01	81	TUNER COMPLETE	*		21047032			3	11.25	A
1	02	81	TUNER UNIT ASSY	*		21047033			3	11.25	A
			21040104		C X	21047034					
1	02	78	TUNER UNIT	*	N	21047037			4		
1	02	81	TUNER UNIT	*		21047038			3	18.00	A
2	01	81	P/B TUNER UNIT.	*		21047041			4		A
2	01	80	VHF/UHF TUNER ASSY.	*	J	21047042			4		
2	02	74	TUNER UNIT	*		21047043				8.74	A
2	02	75	TUNER UNIT	*	N	21050007			4		
			21820057		C X	21050065					
2	00	P	TUNER UNIT			21050069			D	14.88	
			12420384		C X	21051					
1	02	79	TUNER UNIT	*		21057001			3	11.25	A
			21047021		C X	21057002					
2	01	80	TUNER UNIT (P.BUTN)	*		21057003				15.00	A
2	01	80	TUNER & P/B UNIT	*		21057007				15.00	A
			21047021		Z	21057008					
1	01	79	TUNER UNIT (P/B)	*		21057009			3	15.00	A
1	01	82P	VARICAP.TUNER UNIT.	*		21057011			3	9.37	A
2	02	81	UHF TUNER COMPLETE	*		21057012			3	15.00	A
1	02	81	TUNER & P/B COMPLETE	*		21057014			3	11.25	A
			21820057		C X	21057015					
2	02	81	TUNER UNIT ASSY.	*	J	21057016			4		A
			21057011		C X	21057017					
1	01	82	VARICAP TUNER&PANEL.	*		21057018			3	12.21	A
1	00	P	UHF VARICAP TUNER	*		21057021			3	11.11	A
			12437003		C X	21059					
			12477001		C X	21092					
			10190008		C X	21100958					
2	01	77	POT. 5K OHM LIN	*		211306000351				1.09	
2	01	81	POTENTIOMETER	*		211306200002				0.64	
			211310303159		C X	211310100256					
2	00	99	RES. 8.2M OHM 5%	*		211310303159				0.06	
2	01	81	RESISTOR	*		211325604251				0.19	
2	02	99	RES 220 OHM 5%	*		211325604304				0.24	
1	01	99	RES 10 OHM 10%	*		211327100051				0.19	
2	04	75	POT. 5K OHM LOG	*		211335700005				1.53	
2	03	74	POTENTIOMETER	*		211337600002				0.52	
2	01	81	POTENTIOMETER	*		211337700037				0.54	
			10127016		C X	211337700038					
2	02	99	POTENTIOMETER	P	*		211338000001				0.43	
2	02	77	POT. 4.7K OHM LIN	*		211338100001				0.39	
2	02	99	POT. 250K OHM LIN	*		211338100002				0.39	
			40320081		C X	21200686					
			35830078		C X	21200726					
			24910031		C X	21200728					
			44720042		C X	21200738					
			44720028		C X	21200747					
			36170045		C X	21200749					
			52870041		C X	21200752					
			41330147		C X	21200831					
			24940033		C X	21200885					
			31027036		C X	21200957					
			52870186		C X	21201012					
			13440078		C X	21201018					
2	00	81	DET UNIT	*		21210049				6.00	
1	02	77	IF PANEL	*		21217001				19.35	
2	02	77	TB PANEL LESS VALVES	*		21217002				4.27	
2	02	80	PANEL	*		21217004				17.40	

Fig. 7.3 Offset-litho copy

If more than one color is desired, a separate master plate for each color is prepared, and each requires a separate run through the offset machine.

Other types of offset-litho plates are metal (very thin sheets of aluminum) and photographic plates. Paper plates, as we said before, give up to 1000 copies of good quality. Metal plates are capable of producing up to 50,000 of very good quality. Photographic plates can be used indefinitely and the quality is excellent—comparable to that of "old-fashioned" hot-metal typesetting or modern photocomposing.

The cost of acquiring an offset machine is not much more than that of a comparable photocopier, and the cost per copy can be considerably less, depending on the number of copies made. Printing speeds for offset litho are upward of 150 copies per minute, depending on the model of machine. A typist or clerk can be trained to operate the equipment in a half day or less.

There are a number of optional features available for the equipment that makes it attractive for many types of systems jobs. Some examples are perforating, adding a facsimile signature as the copies are printed, or numbering as the copies are printed. Numbering can be forward, backward, skip-two, skip-three, duplicate, or triplicate. Attachments are available for jogging piles of copies into neat stacks and for automatic collating.

MICROFILM

Microfilm is a computer output media in its own right, and as such is described in detail in Chapter 9. It should be mentioned here, however, that microfilm can be used as a method of copying hardcopy computer output, either for long-term storage or for distribution and daily use. Microfilm equipment can be purchased, leased, or for relatively low-volume work, used on a service bureau basis.

For storing records over a long period of time, whether for historical or legal reasons, microfilm has several strong advantages over paper. One is that for large volumes it is very cheap, both in terms of the media itself and, because it is compact, in terms of storage costs. Another lies in its durability and long life.

Accessing microfilm on a regular basis is discussed in detail in Chapter 9. Suffice it to say here that the possible drawbacks are the need for special viewers and the need for training to use them. Advantages are fast retrieval of individual records, low cost when volumes are high, fast production and therefore rapid distribution of updated material, and lower distribution costs as compared to paper copies.

AUTOMATIC PHOTOCOMPOSITION

Automatic photocomposition is not really a method of copying computer output, being, rather, a specialized printing technique. It is mentioned here because it may be the method of choice for producing from computer-processed data extremely large numbers of copies of high quality, that is, quantities in excess of 100,000 of quality comparable to that of printed books.

Information production has been revolutionized from time to time throughout history by relatively simple inventions. The first was, of course, the invention of movable type by Gutenberg. Images of characters were cast on metal slugs, which were arranged into words, lines, and pages. The type was locked into a frame to form a "plate" for printing a page. A major advance over the tedious process of handsetting, character by character, was the linotype machine, which included a typewriterlike keyboard enabling an entire line of type to be cast as one metal slug. It was then only necessary to arrange the lines in a frame to form the page. Photoengraving followed the invention of photography very rapidly. The typeset "page" can be photographed and the negative used to create a solid plate for printing. This is done by fixing the photographic film over a metal plate, and then washing it with acids that etch away the metal except where protected by the photographic emulsion, producing a raised-image plate for printing. It is thus possible to include both line drawings and narrative text on the same page, and the printed image is of better quality than if taken from typeset plates. Given the technique of photoengraving, the next logical step is to project the desired print image directly onto film, omitting the hot-metal type altogether. Hence the invention of the photocomposer.

Many photocomposers operate on an optical principle, with a beam of light projected through a matrix to cast the beam in the shape of the desired character onto film, exposing it. The mechanism automatically advances the film to position it for each character and each line. Newer photocomposers use a cathode-ray tube, with the characters projected electronically onto the face of the tube for photographing. Speeds range from 5 cps for slow optical photocomposers to 6000 cps for fast electronic photocomposers. The exposed film is then developed and plates made as described above.

The relevance of all of this to our discussion should now become evident. The only possible way of driving a photocomposer at a speed of thousands of characters per second is with magnetic tape, and the fastest way of producing the magnetic tape along with all the control information required for the photocomposer is by computer. Most photocomposers are driven either by a paper tape, for the slower ones, or by magnetic tape if of the faster type. Indeed, the fact that material such as census figures, electoral rolls, and business and scientific statistics are often processed by computer has given impetus to the development of techniques for getting the data from the computer to the printed page by the fastest possible means.

The purpose of this discussion has been to make the reader aware of the existence of automatic photocomposition and to sketch in, in the broadest strokes, the technology involved. Software and systems considerations for automatic photocomposition are not within the scope of this book. It is a specialist's subject falling more properly within the printing profession than within data processing as such. Readers seeking more technical information should refer to the second reference in the Bibliography.

CHOOSING A COPYING METHOD

Returning to more lowly considerations of making copies of computer-produced hardcopy output, the methods to be considered will usually be photocopying versus dye-line copying versus spirit duplication versus offset litho. Hand in hand with choosing the type of equipment must be the decision of whether to purchase it, to lease it, or to use a service bureau. A summary of the criteria for making the choice will be found in Figure 7.4.

The following formula will provide a guideline for doing the costing part of the exercise:

X minutes of computer time at $ per hour
+ X cost of master plates or originals
+ X number of copies at   cents per sheet
+ X hours of operator time at $ per hour
+ X hours of copying equipment time at $ per hour
+ cost of ink or other supplies

Sum and divide by the number of copies to arrive at cost per copy.

To calculate the cost of the equipment per hour, it is first necessary to know the monthly rental or the purchase price. Rental is obtained by dividing the number of hours a month the equipment will be in use

Number of copies required, now and in the future
Cost per copy
Capital cost of equipment
Quality of reproduction
Speed of reproduction
Size of pages, original and copies
Reduction-enlargement requirements
Number of colors required
Operator availability and training
Handling after copying
Other types of documents to be copied
    bound
    double sided
    translucent
    colored or graphic

Fig. 7.4   Criteria for choice of copying method

and adding a percentage for electricity and other overheads (the company accountant can supply the percentage). When using the purchase price, a life of five years is assumed, or the company accountant can supply the life span assumed for depreciation purposes, which is divided by the hours of use for an hourly rate, and adding a percentage for overheads.

The calculations are significantly simplified when a service bureau is being considered. Their prices include all costs associated with the equipment and cost of the paper for the copies. It is only necessary to add computer time and costs of sending the masters to the bureau and picking up the finished copies.

Cost per copy is only one of the factors that will influence the final decision. The time needed to make the copies will often be just as important, if not more so. To calculate this, the rated speeds of the computer printer and of the copying equipment are used and a large percentage is added for setup, takedown, refueling of ink supplies, adjusting the equipment, and other contingencies. A percentage of 100 percent would not be overly pessimistic. The results will provide figures with which to compare the choices, but should not be taken as the actual time needed from start to finish of the job. That will depend on the time of day, distribution, other work to be done by the machine and by the operator, and so on.

For each of the choices being considered, these calculations can be done for the average expected work load—that is, number of copies from number of masters in a typical run—and for the maximum. If the volumes are not known exactly or if they can vary greatly, it is best to do the costing and timing on minimum, average, and maximum volumes. The reason for this is important and can make the difference between a wise choice and a bad one. For some copying methods the cost per copy goes down significantly as the number of copies to be made goes up. Similarly, if setting up the copying run is lengthy compared to printing time, the time per copy can go down as the number of copies wanted goes up. An economic choice for 500 copies per master can be a very expensive one for 5 copies per master and vice versa.

CHAPTER 8

Ancillary Forms Operations

Computer printer output can rarely be used in its "raw" form as it comes from the computer room. Continuous forms need a number of operations performed on them before they are ready for distribution and use. The types of operations required and how long they will take will depend on the type of form and its ultimate use. Typical applications require from four to a dozen separate handling operations before the documents are dispatched.

The systems designer should be concerned with ancillary operations, specifying the procedures, the equipment being used, the sequence of operations, and their timing. Too often this task is neglected. Chapter 1 contained several cautionary tales illustrating the effects of such neglect, which can range from inconvenient and inefficient operation of the new system up to and including complete failure of the system to achieve its objectives. Delays and errors in ancillary operations can have even more serious effects; for example, there can be loss of customer good will, loss of competitive position, and indirect financial consequences such as deterioration of cash flow. The dictionary definition of "ancillary" is "subservient or subordinate," but because the system is only as good as its weakest part, these procedures can be very important to the success of the whole system.

The purpose of this chapter is to give a broad overview of the types of operations that might be required, the kinds of equipment available for performing them, and the major factors involved in the processing. As in other parts of the book where equipment is described, no attempt is made to give a complete catalog of machinery. Although the basic operations that need to be performed on continuous forms remain

90

static, new equipment is coming onto the market at an ever-increasing rate.

Types of ancillary operations are summarized in Figure 8.1. The major categories chosen are continuous forms handling, up to the point where they have been burst and are no longer continuous; preparing reports, which should be taken to mean catalogs and similar documents; mailing; and miscellaneous items that do not fit neatly into any other category. They will be discussed in the sequence given in Figure 8.1.

Continuous forms handling
    decollating
    slitting
    bursting
    interstacking
    trimming
    folding
    gluing
    imprinting

Preparing Reports
    document copying
    cutting
    punching holes
    collating
    binding

Mailing
    addressing
    folding
    perforating
    inserting
    sealing
    franking

Miscellaneous
    numbering
    counting
    signing
    laminating
    package tying
    shredding

Fig. 8.1 Ancillary operations

CONTINUOUS FORMS HANDLING

All output coming from the computer printer will be continuous forms. Most will need decollating, bursting, and trimming. Other possible operations, depending on the application, are interstacking, slitting, folding, gluing, and imprinting. Bursting and trimming the margins can sometimes be omitted if the unburst forms are to be bound in special continuous forms binders, described below. Folding, gluing, and imprinting may be separate steps performed after the forms are decollated and burst, but they are included in the category of continuous forms handling because the operations can sometimes be carried out simultaneously.

The photograph in Figure 8.2 illustrates a typical decollating machine. Units can be added in groups of two to handle up to eight-part forms. The machine in the illustration will handle up to four-part forms. Loading the machine and setting the controls at the start of the run

Fig. 8.2   High-speed decollator. Lamson Paragon Model 284 (Courtesy Lamson Paragon.)

take about a minute. Operation is automatic thereafter. Both sprocket-hole margins can be slit off at the same time, and there is also an adjustable center slitter for dividing two-up forms. The decollated parts refold into flat packs, and the one-time carbon is wound onto spindles for disposal. The speed of this model varies from 150 to 250 feet per minute according to the weight of the paper.

Other types of decollators offer various other features. Sprocket holes can be left on some copies, or two parts of a multipart set can be left together, undecollated, for example. The machines are adjustable to take forms of different widths. Smaller, less expensive models decollate only one part at a time.

Bursters separate the decollated forms into single sheets. A burster in operation is shown in Figure 8.3. Speeds vary depending on the model of the machine and the weight of the paper, but a typical range is 110 to 500 feet per minute. They are adjustable for different widths and depths of forms. Slitting margins and two-up forms can be per-

Fig. 8.3 High-speed burster. Mail-Mech PFE 1184. Detail of bursting top copies of printout and stacking separately from other copies (Courtesy Mailing and Mechanization and Printed Forms Equipment, Ltd.)

formed by the burster if it was not done during decollating. Interstacking, that is, collating two different forms, can be done as the pages are burst. Sometimes this is a standard feature of the burster; sometimes a separate attachment must be purchased. Burst stacks of paper in the stacking tray can be automatically jogged to form neat piles.

The "computer manager's dream," as the advertising brochures say, is a machine that both bursts and decollates in the same operation. These can be set up to operate in various ways for example, decollating all parts but bursting only one or two; trimming only some parts; center slitting some parts but not others; and so on. A number of optional accessories are available. One is an imprinter with exchangeable rubber plates so that different graphic symbols can be printed as the forms are processed—for example, the company logo or an advertising slogan. The ink is fast drying and will not smear. Attachments can be added for folding, gluing, or counting as the forms are processed.

Safety features of these machines include microswitch covers so that the machine cannot be operated while the covers are raised; fast braking if the operator detects a fault in the operation; and a "jam detector" to stop the machine automatically if trouble occurs while it is running unattended.

PREPARING REPORTS

Once the forms are decollated, trimmed, and burst, it may be necessary to bind them into folders or books for ease of use and storage. Operations associated with this may include copying, cutting or slicing, punching holes, and collating.

Document copying methods have been covered in detail in the previous chapter. It only remains to be said that if collating is required at that stage of the processing, it is possible to obtain an automatic collator as an accessory to a copying or offset-litho machine. This is often in the form of a drum that operates in synchronization with the ejection of the copies from the machine. As the copies are ejected, the drum turns so that each page drops into the next pocket. It can be set for up to several hundred copies, depending on the device. It only remains for the operator to take the collated sets out of the pockets of the drum when the run is finished.

Alternately, collating can be done as a separate step. Hand collating, of course, requires no equipment other than a large work table.

Pages are laid out in sequence to make up the stacks. This is obviously very slow, tedious, and error prone; it is suitable only for low volumes of work. A semiautomatic collator can speed up the process somewhat. One version on the market has a number of horizontal shelves, one for each page of the report. The pages are ejected a few inches, one at a time in sequence, for the operator to pick up and stack; or, a fully automatic machine can be installed for high-volume work. These also jog the papers into piles with the edges even, ready for the operator to pick them up one at a time for the next operation.

There may be a requirement, either before or after the pages are collated, to trim or slice them. This may be to remove margins or separate two-up forms if that was not done during decollating or bursting, or to remove extra unwanted portions of paper. For small quantities a hand-operated paper cutter (guillotine) will suffice. Larger volumes call for a power-driven cutter. This device should be equipped with a safety mechanism to ensure that the operator cannot be injured. One model, for example, can be activated only by pushing two buttons simultaneously, one with each hand, and holding them down for the entire operating cycle. If either button is released, the knife stops moving instantly, thus making accidental injury virtually impossible. In other models the machine cannot be started until safety shields have been lowered into place.

A hole-punching operation is often unnecessary for continuous computer forms if one or both of the sprocket-hole margins is left intact; or specifically designed preprinted forms may have binding holes prepunched, as in Figure 5.3 in Chapter 5. Many stationers supply binders for stock continuous forms in a range of popular sizes. Most are suitable for either burst or unburst paper. One widely available line of binders incorporates flexible nylon posts that are pushed through the sprocket holes at either side and then bent over and secured. A range of racks, storage bins, cabinets, and trolleys can provide a complete "system" for transport, storage, and access of the bound reports.

A visit to any large stationer will supply other ideas for binding reports. A plastic thong or comb binding is one possibility. This method allows the pages to be opened flat, like a loose-leaf binder, but the pages are permenently secured to prevent them from getting out of sequence or lost. A special device is available for punching the holes and inserting the comb. Other possibilities are plastic spines clamped along one margin, with cardboard or plastic covers, or gumming with a special adhesive to form pads.

MAILING

Direct mail and mechanization of mail handling are specialized subjects in their own right. Any large organization must, almost by definition, be a heavy user of the postal system. Some companies advertise by direct mail, sell their products by mail, or send out huge quantities of material to customers and potential customers. Examples are magazine publishers, mail order stores, and book clubs. A systems analyst new to this area, who is working on a project with computer output that will eventually find its way into the postal system, should find out what equipment and expertise already exist in the company. This should be one of the first steps, in fact, because there may be possibilities for taking advantage of slack time on existing equipment if the output forms are designed properly.

Addressing the envelope is one major problem to be solved. Hand-written or typewritten addresses are out of the question for all but the smallest quantities. One obvious solution being used more and more is window envelopes. All that is required is care in positioning the name and address on the insert, and in folding and inserting, so that the printing shows through the window. The size of the envelope has to be coordinated with the folded size of the insert; inserts too small for the envelope can slip so that the address is no longer visible.

Another solution for personally addressed mail has been devised by some suppliers of continuous stationery. The multipart set consists of a top copy that shows all details printed for retention in the company. This is backed with a patch of carbon so that only the name and address appear on the next page, which is the outside of an envelope. The envelopes are in the form of continuous stationery for bursting later. Carbon patches on the inner side of the envelope allow the printed details to appear on a slip of paper inside the envelope, which is presealed. Other items can be included in the envelope when the sets are made, for example, a postage-paid reply card. Forms handling consists of taking the finished job from the computer room, decollating to remove the top page, and bursting to separate the envelopes. If an arrangement with the post office for an appropriate license has been made, no stamping or franking operation is required. All steps of folding, inserting, and sealing are thus bypassed. Stationery of this type is expensive, obviously, but for large volumes might be justified.

If the insert is not personally addressed to the recipient, which is often the case with direct mail advertising, addressing the envelope calls for a different solution. Some possibilities follow.

Embossed Metal Plates. Embossed metal plates are cheap and durable, and they can be used many times. The plates are embossed on a special machine with a keyboard similar to that of a typewriter. A tab can be positioned at the top of each plate so that the automatic imprinting machine can select some plates and reject others during the print run. Printing can be onto labels, envelopes, magazine wrappers, and the like.

Dye-Line or Spirit Duplicating. The masters for dye-line or spirit duplication will eventually wear out. How many impressions can be taken from any one master depends on the type of materials used. Dye-line and spirit duplication were discussed in detail in Chapter 7.

Automatic Typing. Labels or continuous forms envelopes can be addressed with an automatic typewriter driven by punched cards, paper tape, or magnetic cards or tape. This is often a feasible alternative to printing labels with the computer printer; it is slower but not nearly as expensive.

Computer-Printed Labels. Gummed and pressure-sensitive labels as continuous forms were described in Chapter 5. Machines are available that will separate the labels and stick them onto envelopes or wrappers automatically and very rapidly. Labels may also be the method of choice for packages. A label can be produced as part of a set that includes the customer's order; it can then accompany the documentation while the order is being assembled, and, finally, be attached to the outside of the package after the package has been wrapped.

Folding, inserting, and sealing are other steps in the output handling process. It is possible to buy separate machines for each of these operations, or one machine that performs them all, automatically, and in addition perforates the insert (for return coupon advertising, for example), counts the items, and stacks them or ejects them directly into mailbags for dispatch to the post office. Speeds in excess of 6000 items per hour per machine can be attained.

The final step is postage for the envelope. This can be preprinted under license from the post office, franked, or stamped. There are a number of models of postage meters available; the larger ones are almost entirely automatic. A degree of control is needed to ensure that the machine is not misused. For some direct mail campaigns it is considered desirable to use a postage stamp to further "personalize" the look of the letter. If this is a requirement of the system, the stamping operation can be entirely automatic if the appropriate machine is acquired.

MISCELLANEOUS OPERATIONS

In the category of miscellaneous operations we include a handful of operations that may be desirable for certain applications. They are numbering, counting, signing, laminating, package tying, and shredding.

Automatic numbering of forms has already been mentioned in this chapter in other contexts. Almost any machine that performs one or more operations on the output one sheet at a time can also be fitted with an attachment that will number serially. These include bursters and decollators, copying machines, and collators; or numbering can be done as a separate step either by hand or automatically. Hand stampers are available that will number serially, skipping one, skipping two, skipping three, duplicate, triplicate, and so on. The date and even the time of day can be added at the same time, or the imprint can include the company logo or an advertising slogan. Numbering large quantities of single sheets should be done automatically, as part of another operation if possible, but hand numbering can be useful for copies of bound reports and other low-volume work.

There are several places in the ancillary handling sequence where counting can be done at the same time. Almost all copying machines and postage meters include a counter as a standard fixture. They can also be fitted to other devices, including the burster or the folding machine.

Automatic signing machines are standard appliances in many offices. It is possible with such a machine to produce "hand-signed" letters quickly and economically in large quantities. Check-writing machines also add one or two signatures to the check, but it is necessary to make an arrangement with the bank in advance before using this type of equipment. These devices must be subject to strict controls. Most models require a key to activate them and use a removable signature plate that can be stored in the company safe when not in use. An automatic counter provides a further measure of control. Provided the appropriate controls exist, signing checks after printing by computer is usually more secure than using presigned ones as continuous forms. (A more detailed discussion of this and other aspects of the security of output will be found in Chapter 18.)

Laminating is the process of sealing a card or document inside a plastic envelope. It is permanent, and any attempt to remove the plastic will damage the contents. A relatively inexpensive machine is available to do the job. Lamination can be a useful feature for documents such as employee identification cards, certificates of attendance, passes, pages of a code book or instruction manual, or any paper that receives constant handling and must last a long time.

Another miscellaneous piece of equipment that might be useful for certain jobs is a package-tying machine. Models are on the market that will take virtually any size package, parcel, or bundle of papers, and tie it securely with string, both ways, neatly knotted, in seconds.

Finally, another device, the use of which is discussed in the chapter on confidential output, is the paper shredder or "automatic waste paper basket." If any of the output is confidential, ancillary forms handling is the first area outside of the computer room where protection measures are required. Disposal of one-time carbon, spoiled copies, and unwanted copies can constitute a weak link in the security system if the scrap paper is not destroyed. An electric shredder is clean, almost silent, and provides a method of immediate disposal, all advantages over the alternative of collecting such scrap for burning.

SUMMARY

This chapter has given an overview of the kinds of equipment available for ancillary forms handling. The selection of devices described has been representative but by no means exhaustive. Almost any paper-handling operation can be automated at very high speeds if the volumes and time constraints for delivery to the user can justify the expense of the equipment. It is up to the systems analyst to design and specify the procedures needed for hard-copy output from the system, and to investigate the kinds of equipment that are available, or will be needed, for handling it.

CHAPTER 9

Computer Output to Microfilm

Computer output to microfilm (COM) is an alternative to producing high-volume reports as hard copy from a printer. The operation of a computer output to microfilm system is shown in outline in Figure 9.1. The basic steps are as follows:

1. Production of the formatted report as magnetic tape records
2. Use of the tape as input on an off-line device, the microfilm recorder, to produce film (This is done by converting the digital signals from the tape to analog signals, forming the characters on a cathode-ray tube, and photographing the image formed. This is done automatically at very high speed.)
3. Development of the film (This is usually a wet process, but does not require a darkroom nor special skills on the part of the operator.)
4. On yet another piece of equipment, duplication of the film and creation of microfiche or cassette reels (As many copies as desired can be made, one at a time.)
5. Removal of the film to archival storage or distribution for use in microfilm viewers, or both, as required

Fuller technical details will be given later in the chapter. It should be pointed out now, however, that it is also possible to produce microfilm on-line; the recorder can operate at CPU speeds or faster, so the intermediate step of preparing a tape is eliminated.

100

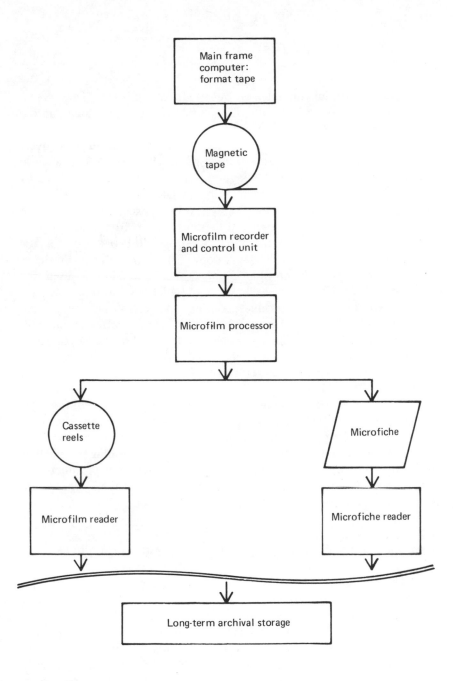

Fig. 9.1 Computer output to microfilm system outline

EXAMPLE APPLICATIONS

Any batch application requiring high-volume output readable by humans is a potential computer output to microfilm system. Two typical applications are described in outline here: a banking system and a stock control system.

In the banking system, customer accounts are updated daily overnight at the central computer installation, which serves 320 branches. There are three types of input: magnetic character recognition (MICR) for checks, optical character recognition (OCR) for the bulk of other transactions, and punched cards for low-volume exception data. There are also three types of output: from the line printer, from a graph plotter, and computer output to microfilm. The printer is used for customers' statements and other essential hard copy. The graph plotter produces graphs and charts for top management. The microfilm is used for daily records for the branches, the bulk of which are customer account records. The microfilm is produced on-line and microfiche are created. Each one holds the equivalent of 220 printed pages at a reduction ratio of 42:1 in a space 6 by 4 inches. There are two on-line COM recorders that do the work of 15 line printers. At the branches, portable microfiche viewers are used to answer customers' queries; the customer can view his own record.

In the stock control application, the old batch system required 180 hours of computer time per week to print 116,000 pages that were then bound into books for use by material controllers. The information was four days out-of-date when it reached them. The microfilm system that replaced it requires only 9 hours of computer time, and the microfilm reels reach the controllers the next morning. Moreover, the system has resulted in a saving of about $25,000 per year.

ADVANTAGES AND DISADVANTAGES OF MICROFILM

The examples outlined above illustrate the primary benefits that can be achieved with a change to a microfilm system, namely, faster throughput and cost savings.

The faster throughput results from the high speed of microfilm recorders as opposed to line printers or any other means of hard-copy production. Microfilming speeds of up to 30,000 lines per minute can be obtained. As will be explained in detail below, the recorder operates at electronic as opposed to mechanical speeds and is therefore the fastest output peripheral giving human-readable copies (with some assistance from a viewer) that can be used in a batch mode. The steps involved in developing the film, making copies, possibly cutting the developed film into card format, and distribution are no more time consuming than equivalent forms-handling operations for large printer-produced reports, and they can be faster. There are obvious time savings, for example, in the compactness of the media—a reel of microfilm can be sent by airmail for less than the cost of shipping the same information on paper by parcel post, and it will arrive much sooner.

Cost savings can also be considerable, but these can be realized only if the volume of data produced is high. A general rule of thumb for the break-even point is about 100,000 print pages per month across all applications; any installation producing this much paper in a batch mode could possibly benefit from computer output to microfilm if only on a service bureau basis. At 500,000 pages per month, the crossover point for a full in-house microfilm installation is reached. These are, of course, only very rough guidelines; it would always be necessary to do a full-scale feasibility study for any specific project.

Other benefits of computer output to microfilm are faster retrieval time for the user, the possibility of getting an unlimited number of "top" copies, and the flexibility of upper and lower-case alphanumerics, graphic capability, and so on.

On the other hand there are some very real limitations to the use of microfilm for computer output. One of the major ones is its unsuitability for volatile data and real-time processing. Updating usually requires a complete rerun; although it is possible to splice new records into the microfilm reel, it is a time-consuming and error-prone operation. Computer output to microfilm can thus be thought of as a replacement for or alternative to only those batch systems that have high-volume static printer-produced output.

Another problem with microfilm is the cost, both tangible and intangible, of a change over to a new method of working. To realize full cost savings, microfilm usually must be thought of as an alternative to the line printer, cutting across all applications, rather than as a method for use with just one system. That means conversion of old systems as well as a new technique for new ones, with all the usual conversion problems. In addition, because it is a new technique, there will inevitably be resistance to the change. How serious user resistance will be will, of course, vary widely from one organization to another, ranging from negligible at one end of the scale to totally disruptive at the other. In any case, user training will require a larger proportion of the system effort than would be expected if a new technique were not involved.

These and other advantages and disadvantages of computer output to microfilm are summarized in Figure 9.2.

Advantages
    Cost savings; typical claims are savings by a factor of 4 over ordinary line printer output
    Faster throughput
    Faster retrieval of information
    Compactness; typical claims are space savings of factors of 50 to 100; a 100-foot roll of film weighs less than 1 pound and can contain a 2400-page report
    Lower distribution costs due to compactness
    Unlimited number of copies possible; additional copies cost about one-third less than line printer copies
    Fewer ancillary operations required than with paper
    Graphics, and lower-case options feasible
        variable type faces

Disadvantages
    Unsuitable for real-time update and volatile data
    Updating possible only by creating new film
    Usual conversion difficulties
    Unfamiliarity; possible user resistance; training required
    Risk of disruption due to mechanical breakdown
    Relatively long setup time for film processing; wet film processing may affect operator training and job assignments
    Microfilm readers may be inconvenient to bifocal wearers
    High initial investment in equipment
    High volume needed to achieve cost benefits

Fig. 9.2 Advantages and disadvantages of computer output to microfilm

ON-LINE VERSUS OFF-LINE

Although some experts are of the opinion that an on-line microfilm system is rarely, if ever, justified, a number of user installations have opted for it with success. The major configuration difference is that with the on-line recorder used as a peripheral to the main-frame computer, the intermediate step of producing a magnetic tape is eliminated, achieving very rapid throughput. Computer time required will be no more, and probably less. On-line output to microfilm is thus often cheaper than off-line. In some cases programming changes may not even be required; software supplied by the microfilm equipment manufacturer takes care of the interface, and the problem program can treat the recorder like any other peripheral.

A major drawback of on-line output to microfilm, on the other hand, is that if there is a fault in the recorder such that the film is unusable, this will not be known until the run is over, and the entire job will have to be rerun. If the system were off-line, no extra computer time would be required. There are also disadvantages in wet-film processing, which may require plumbing connections and the use of chemical liquids, not a desirable feature for the computer room. In addition, computer operators will have to be trained in new setup, monitoring and takedown procedures. Finally, some manufacturers offer only a limited range of options with on-line recorders.

THE TECHNOLOGY OUTPUT TO MICROFILM

This chapter began with an overview of how computer output to microfilm works. In this section a closer examination is made of its technology, with emphasis on the system designer's options and on choice criteria. Software and other system design considerations will be covered in a separate section following this discussion of technology.

The Computer Output Microfilm Recorder

In an on-line system, digital signals from the CPU go directly to the microfilm recorder and are fed through logic circuits for interpretation. The only difference in an off-line recorder is that the digital signals come from a magnetic tape; the tape unit can be an integral part of the recorder. In either case the interpreted signals then feed an image formation unit. There are three types of image formation techniques in use; cathode-ray tube (CRT), electron beam, and light-emitting diode (LED). The cathode-ray tube is by far the most widely used, and will be described first.

A diagrammatic representation of cathode-ray tube image recording is shown in Figure 9.3. A frame ("page") of data is generated onto the face of the tube. This image is focused through lenses to give the appropriate reduction ration (usually 24X, 42X, or 48X) onto photo-

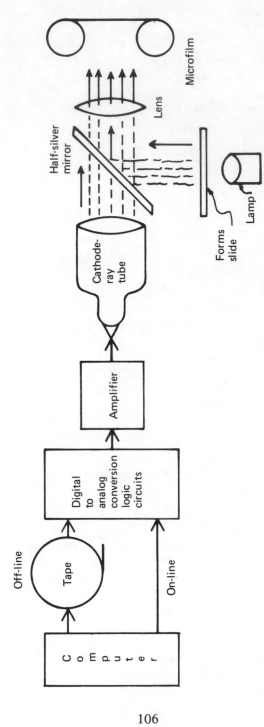

Fig. 9.3 Cathode-ray tube microfilm recording

graphic film in an automatic camera. A forms slide can be interposed to combine with the variable data for the final image. Once exposed, the film is automatically advanced to the next frame. Speeds of up to 120,000 cps can be attained on the fastest recorders.

Methods of Generating the Image

There are a number of different methods of generating the image into the face of the cathode-ray tube.

Dot Matrix. The dot-matrix method is similar in principle to matrix printers (see Chapter 4) except that the dots are dots of light that form characters. Although reliable, this method is relatively slow and is not widely used today.

Character Generation. With the character-generation method each character is formed by combining lines and curves of predetermined forms. This method requires core memory and a central processor unit, that is, hardware equivalent to a minicomputer.

Vector Generation. The vector-generation method is similar to that of character generation except that the set of lines and curves is infinitely large, being controlled by the programmer who can program lines of any size and shape. This has obvious programming and software cost disadvantages, but it does produce output of very high quality.

The Charactron. The Charactron is a shaped-beam tube developed by one of the largest computer output microfilm equipment manufacturers, DatagraphiX. An electron beam is directed through a shaped plate, or matrix, at the point where the desired character appears on the plate. The plate can be thought of as a template of any required set of characters. The image thus produced is focused into the face of the cathode-ray tube at the appropriate place on the "page" format. The character set in use at any one time is restricted, but the quality of the image and the speed of production are both very high. Most installations require only an alphanumeric capability, as opposed to a graphic one, and so the lack of flexibility may not be restrictive. A DatagraphiX Charactron type recorder is shown in Figure 9.4.

An electron-beam recorder differs from the conventional cathode-ray type in that the beam is focused directly onto specially prepared film. The exposed film is then developed by a heat process and is thus sensitive to extremes of temperature.

The light-emitting diode technique uses no camera as such. Signals are passed along fiber-optic strands to form characters in a matrix, which is then projected onto film. The film is advanced after each line

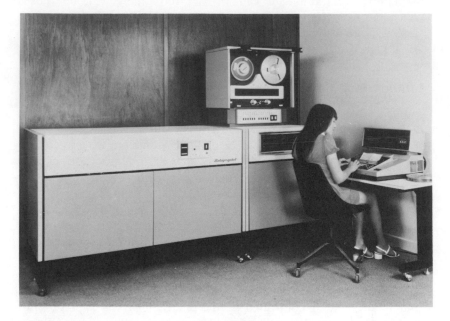

Fig. 9.4   Microfilm recorder (Courtesy DatagraphiX)

is formed, as opposed to once for each frame as with the other methods. Options available on equipment using this method are still limited, although further development work is expected. The light-emitting diode method may in time prove to be cheaper, more reliable, and easier to operate than the others.

FORMAT OF MICROFILM

Microfilm is available in a variety of sizes. Many commercial installations use either 16 mm rolls, or 105 mm rolls, which are then cut to size to form microfiche "pages." Frames can be positioned along the roll in a variety of ways. For example, 16 mm film with a reduction ratio of 24X is recorded in cine mode, one frame after another longitudinally. If 42X reduction is used, the frames can be placed two-up. Thus in the first instance 20 average pages of information can be recorded sequentially on 12 inches of film, and in the second case, about 40 average pages on 12 inches.

The format of a 105-mm microfiche roll, on the other hand, might be 8 frames by 10 (comic mode) at 25X reduction, for a total of 80 frames per fiche; or at 42X reduction, 14 x 16 frames, giving a total of 224 for the fiche. Other variations are possible depending on the size of the film and the options available with the equipment. These examples are illustrated in Figure 9.5.

These and other options are controlled by the operator of the recorder via switches, a plug board, or a job card, depending on the type of equipment in use.

FILM PROCESSING AND DUPLICATION

After filming, the next step is to process the film. This is analogous to developing ordinary camera film to obtain negatives, from which prints are made. In the case of microfilm, although it is altogether possible to go on and make prints—that is, enlarged hard-copy output—this is usually not done because the whole object of the microfilm exercise is to avoid the problems of paper handling.

The film processor is usually a separate unit supplied by the recorder manufacturer. Darkroom conditions are not required. The film magazine, or cassette, is taken from the recorder and loaded into the processor. The processor forms its own darkroom, with the film being automatically developed, stopped, fixed, washed, and dried. Silver halide film is used for recording, so the processing requires the use of chemicals and water. It is this fact that makes on-line processing unattractive. Most processors work at a speed of 5 to 6 feet per minute, although some are faster.

The processed film appears with black letters against a clear background, a positive image. It is possible to reverse the image in duplication, and this is often done to improve readability in the microfilm viewer.

The processed film can now be duplicated, as many copies as required being made. There are two major duplication methods. The first is a diazo process that uses ammonia fumes. The second is a vesicular process, which has the advantage of requiring neither water nor chemicals. The film used has microscopic vesicles (bubbles) embedded in plastic. When exposed to heat, there is a reaction that causes the image to be formed. Roll-to-roll duplication takes place at speeds of 200 to 300 feet per minute. A film processor is shown in Figure 9.6.

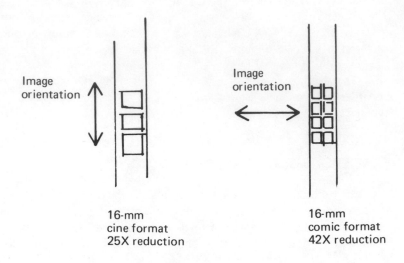

Image orientation

16-mm
cine format
25X reduction

Image orientation

16-mm
comic format
42X reduction

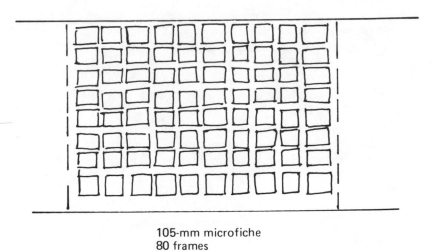

105-mm microfiche
80 frames
25X reduction

Fig. 9.5   Example of microfilm formats

110

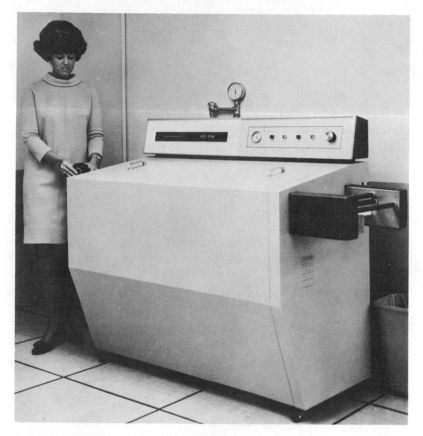

Fig. 9.6   Microfilm processor (Courtesy DatagraphiX)

VIEWING AND REPRODUCTION

A microfiche viewer is shown in Figure 9.7. A wide variety of models are available, along with ancillary equipment like microfiche cutters and mounters, storage and carrying cases for microfiche and reels, and so on. For ease of use it is necessary to have sufficient numbers of viewers and copies of files on microfilm available at convenient locations.

Hard-copy reproduction from microfilm is also possible. This can be done on a batch job basis by data control for wide distribution, or on a one-off basis as and when needed. Some viewers come equipped with a reproduction unit so that the user can obtain a hard-copy reproduction of the page he is viewing on the spot.

Fig. 9.7   Microfiche viewer (Courtesy DatagraphiX)

For multicopy production of high quality, microfilm can be used as input to lithographic printing. A litho master is produced from each frame of microfilm, and as many copies as needed can then be printed. Figure 9.8 shows a platemaker available from DatagraphiX for this purpose.

SYSTEM DESIGN CONSIDERATIONS

The systems analyst needs to be concerned with software and systems problems as much as, or more than, with the technical aspects of microfilm production. Especially important are considerations of

Fig. 9.8 Microfilm platemaker (Courtesy DatagraphiX)

113

graphics and special characters, software, indexing and retrieval methods, updating records and files held on microfilm, page format and layout, and the design and use of forms overlays. Each of these areas will be discussed in turn.

Graphics and Special Characters

Some microfilm recorders have powerful graphics capability. The technology of cathode-ray recorders makes it possible to draw lines of any length, width, and angles anywhere on the face of the tube by means of addressable points. Typically, there is an array of 16,000 by 16,000 addressable points. Standard routines for grids, patterns, drawings of tools and symbols, and so on, can be stored as programmed subroutines and called for as needed, or programmed for the application.

Processes or projections that change with respect to time, for example, effluent pollution in waterways, sales trends, or simulated biological processes, can be projected as a large number of pictures, each one slightly different than the one before, and microfilmed. The film is then treated as a cine film to produce an animated movie.

Not all microfilm recorders have this option. Devices based on the Charactron technique, for example, are restricted to alphanumerics. As a general rule of thumb, graphics equipment is more expensive and slower; graphs can be produced at speeds in the order of 1000 frames per hour, for example, as opposed to 18,000 alphanumeric frames with 64 lines of 132 positions. For engineering and scientific applications, therefore, the graphics feature can be invaluable; but for standard commercial users, lower cost and higher speed may be worth the lack of flexibility. It is often more realistic to use a computer output microfilm service bureau for the small amount of graphical work to be done.

Even with a recorder restricted to alphanumerics, however, there is still a great deal more flexibility than with the high-speed line printer. Many recorders come with standard options for upper- and lower-case characters, foreign language character sets, italic and bold face, and so on, which may be mixed on the same page and on the same line. Forms overlays (discussed below) can then supply the small amount of fixed graphical data that is required.

Software

All major suppliers of computer microfilm equipment also offer standard software packages to go with it. Full use should be made of the available software to keep programming and reprogramming costs to a minimum. Some of the basic routines available from most manufacturers are as follows:

Printing Format to Computer Output Microfilm Format Conversion. Although some recorders will accept tapes with records formatted as for the line printer, better use can be made of computer microfilm features by reformatting for the recorder.

Generation of Eye-Readable Titles. Human-readable titles are of great use for selecting microfiche for viewing. Options usually include a standard title for the file, plus a variable title based on the records shown in that fiche.

Generation of Reel and Fiche Indexes. Whether for use by the human user or automatic retrieval by the viewer, indexing can save time in finding the individual record required. Various indexing techniques will be discussed in more detail below.

System-Out Management. The out system should interface with the operating system to pool data onto disk for later retrieval and formatting.

Indexing and Retrieval

A major systems problem in designing an application of computer output to microfilm is in choosing the method of indexing the reels of film or the microfiche so that the user can find the record he wants easily and quickly. Techniques for use with roll microfilm will be discussed first, followed by identification and indexing methods suitable for microfiche.

Over and above that of inspecting each frame individually, which can be very time consuming, there are three basic methods of identifying and selecting frames from a roll of microfilm. They are eyeball coding, code-line indexing, and image coding for automatic selection. These are all suitable for sequential records arranged serially on the roll.

Eyeball coding involves some kind of mark below or beside each frame to indicate to the user the relative position that frame occupies in the series. A simple method would be to put an identifying code related to the record under each frame—for example, social security number for personnel records or part number for stock control records. This can be done automatically by the microfilm recorder. The user can then advance the roll in the viewer fairly rapidly until he reaches the frame he wants.

Instead of keys, however, it is possible to place indexing lines along the margin of the film in different relative positions, so that as the roll is advanced rapidly the lines seem to rise and fall like an animated cartoon. The user can tell when he is approaching the frame he wants by the position of the mark, and he can then slow down to inspect each frame until he reaches the right one. Code-line indexing can be made semiautomatic by using a viewer that "counts" the frames and displays the frame number on a counter.

Image-control coding for fully automatic selection is possible with some types of equipment. A document mark is placed under each frame by the recorder. The user is given a master index showing the numerical position of each record; he keys the position of the frame he wants into the viewer, and the viewer then electronically counts off the frame and stops the roll at the right position. A variation on this is available with the Kodak Miracode system. A binary code descriptor is recorded next to each frame (thus reducing the number of frames per roll); the user keys in the desired reference number and the viewer searches out and displays the frame, regardless of its location on the roll. Any frame on the roll can be accessed in 10 seconds or less. Illustrations of these types of retrieval codes are given in Figure 9.9.

Various methods of eyeball coding and indexing are also possible for microfiche. Some alternatives are illustrated in Figure 9.10 and discussed below.

Titling of each fiche in large characters that are readable by the unaided eye can be done by the recorder. Titling is triggered by codes on the source tape or by software routines. The title is usually two lines occupying one column of frames along the width of the fiche (see Figure 9.10), thus reducing the number of data frames accordingly. The title can consist of sequential fiche number, a file or report name or number, a reference code related to the data on the fiche, or some combination of these. Each frame on the fiche can also be titled with an eye-readable code identifying the frame number within the fiche by row and column.

Many microfiche applications use some method of indexing in addition to eye-readable titles and codes. Indexing methods are similar in concept to the sequential or indexed sequential retrieval methods that are used for disk files. There are many possible variations, limited only by the ingenuity of the systems designer; one will be described here. The application is stock control with product records held on microfiche. There are 10,000 products, each one requiring one frame. At 42X reduction with titles, 49 microfiche will be required. There is one addi-

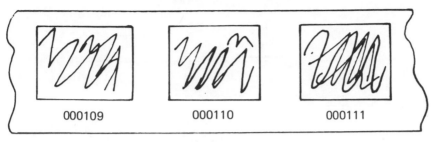

000109　　　　　000110　　　　　000111

Eyeball coding

Code-line indexing

Image-control coding

Kodak Miracode binary coding

Fig. 9.9　Microfilm roll retrieval codes

117

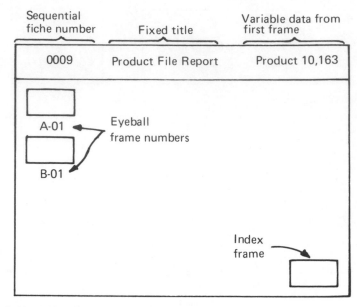

Fig. 9.10   Microfiche coding and indexing

tional microfiche containing the indexes in two levels. This is illustrated in Figure 9.11. The user first selects the master index microfiche and views the first frame, scanning it to find the group within which the required product number lies. He then goes to the frame indicated and scans that to find the product number. The entry shows the fiche number and frame number containing the product information he is looking for.

Updating

As was mentioned previously, microfilm is a batch-oriented media not suitable as an alternative to an on-line system. Although access to data can be, for all practical purposes, as fast as on-line access through a terminal, the data cannot be updated in an on-line mode. Microfilm must therefore be thought of as a substitute for hard-copy output where continuous updating is not required.

It can be faster and cheaper, however, to issue new reports from updated files with microfilm than with hard-copy output. More frequent production can mean that the user has data that is more current at any time than would be possible otherwise.

With very large volumes of data, issuing a completely new listing

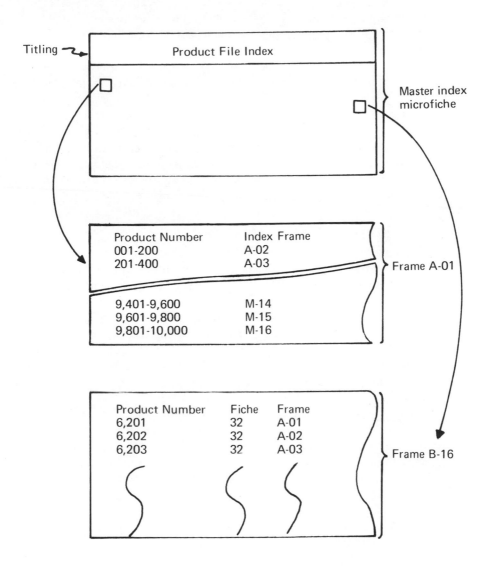

Fig. 9.11 Microfiche indexing example

119

at frequent intervals can still be prohibitively expensive. The indexing techniques described above can be expanded to overcome this difficulty. To go back to the example, let us say that 2 percent of the stock records require updating each day. When computer processing is completed, a tape formatted for microfilm is produced, but the tape contains only those records that have been updated or corrected in that run. Instead of producing a completely new set of 50 microfiche, only two new ones are required—one containing the new data and one with a revised index. Thus when the user accesses the index fiche, he is led to the new data fiche rather than the old one with the out-of-date record. For those familiar with indexed sequential disk files, the new fiche can be thought of as analogous to an overflow area on disk. "Reorganization," or the production of a completely new set of microfiche, would take place at predefined intervals depending on how many of the records had been updated.

Page Layout and Forms Overlays

The systems analyst has many more options in designing microfilm record layouts than when designing line-printer reports. Graphics capability, choice of type fonts, and upper- and lower-case characters have already been mentioned.

Microfilm offers the further option of right justification of text. This can be done as an extra step in formatting the tape records during computer processing. Words and letters can be pushed together a little or spread out a little to make each line of print exactly the same length as all other lines, creating output that is as tidy and professional as typeset material. With lines of some length, say, the standard 132-character line of the printer, hyphenation is not necessary. In any case, programming for hyphenation of words is complicated and time consuming, and the results are never as satisfactory as hand-set type requiring human intelligence. Right justification is not necessary for columnar reports, but it should be considered for narrative material, especially when the resulting microfilm is to be used as input to a printing process for mass dissemination of information.

With the exceptions mentioned in this chapter, rules and guidelines for designing the page layout and the forms overlays are similar to those for printer-produced reports and preprinted continuous forms. A full discussion of designing these can be found in Chapters 5 and 6.

PART THREE

REMOTE AND ON-LINE OUTPUT

CHAPTER 10

Principles of Real-Time Systems

In a full real-time system, input data is submitted for processing as the events that create the data occur: Files are updated with the data at once; any errors detected are referred back to the originator for correction at once; and the user receives output and answers to inquiries without any significant delay. To do this it is necessary to have the main computer on-line during working hours—which may be around the clock—and to have it linked to input and output devices that may be geographically remote from the computer center. This in turn requires a heavy commitment to hardware for handling communications between the computer and the users and to software to support the communication. A real-time system thus differs from batch processing in two very significant ways: input, processing, and output are much more closely linked, both in time and in logical complexity; and the new types of hardware and software require new and different systems knowledge and skills. The approach to the subject of output in this part of the book must therefore be somewhat different from that taken in other sections.

The first two chapters of this section cover the principles of real time; data transmission, whether it be outwards from the computer or inwards from terminals; and communications hardware, including terminals, for handling the transmission. A basic knowledge of these subjects is a prerequisite for learning to design a real-time system. Although they are not "output" subjects per se, they must be mastered for an adequate understanding of the output aspects of a real-time system. The chapters in the second half of this section are devoted more strictly to output, covering alphanumeric and graphic output for on-line

123

terminals; but even there, references will be made to input and processing functions, especially as they relate to the design of an interactive system.

Readers with real-time experience may wish to skip over this chapter and the next one. Those without any such experience and those wishing a review of the principles of data transmission and communications technology will find them useful background.

BATCH VERSUS REAL TIME

Conventional or garden variety batch systems, with input collected for processing at a scheduled time and output produced at periodic intervals, can have many basic disadvantages, some of which are listed below.

1. There is a relatively long time gap between submission of prime input data and the receipt of the output by the user, making batch processing suitable only for record-keeping systems in which after-the-fact recording of data is all that is required.
2. Errors made on source documents or in keying can be carried through the system paper flow for several days before the errors are detected and corrected, and the material is resubmitted.
3. The master files never truly reflect the current position. At each update, several days' data may remain outstanding, not having reached the system in time for processing.
4. An ad hoc or one-time request from the user for small quantities of information may take so long to organize and process that the results are of limited value to him when received.
5. The system is designed for certain predefined purposes and its inflexibility means that it cannot be easily modified or extended.
6. There is little impetus for user involvement in the design or the operation of the system, perpetuating the "that is your problem" dichotomy between data processing and user departments, with the resulting friction, bad feeling, and inadequate systems.

It can thus be seen that the major general justifications for any real-time system are in the areas of speed, accuracy, and cost.

Speed

Speed is an obvious factor weighing in favor of on-line processing. Typical output response time to a request for information from the computer files may be in the order of 5 seconds or less. If updating is done on-line too, the data received will be entirely up-to-date. Note that this justification for real-time processing does not hold if a 24-hour turnaround on data three days old is entirely adequate for the user's purposes; the need must exist.

Accuracy

A batch system has many discrete steps in the processing cycle, separated both by time and by distance. An error occurring at any step may well be carried forward to the next. When errors are finally trapped and reported, correction and reinput can be difficult and time consuming. In a real-time system many of the processing steps are combined into one rapid series independent of geographical distance. For example, the creation of a source document, entry of the data through a terminal, validation, correction and reentry, and processing of the corrected data may all take place in a matter of minutes and involve only one individual interacting with the computer system through the terminal. Speed can generate accuracy.

Cost

Large real-time systems have a "public image" of being very expensive. They can and often are fully justified solely on tangible cost savings, however. For example, tangible benefits can accrue from savings on clerical procedures, reduced inventories and stock holdings, and time and consumable products in data preparation. This is not to say that intangible benefits are not also important; increased customer service, better and more accurate management information, and an up-to-date company image are all desirable, but cost-saving figures cannot be attached to them, and a system with *only* these benefits may be no more than expensive window dressing.

In summary, the advantages of a real-time system can include concurrent submission of data and receipt of output; detection of input errors at the time the error is made and immediate correction; immediate update of master files; inquiries made on the spot and the answers received immediately, either displayed or printed; and user involvement with direct input and output with a resulting increase in his concern for the success of the system.

On the other hand there are some very real drawbacks to real-time processing as a number of organizations have discovered to their cost and sorrow. First, there is almost always the need for greater reliance on outside agencies, including hardware and software suppliers and common carriers, without an equal measure of control. Failure is less predictable and harder to correct. A major drawback for many potential real-time users is the requirement for a much greater investment in equipment and running costs than is necessary for batch processing. Associated with this are higher staff training costs and more expensive backup or fallback facilities. And a final obstacle may be the human one: resistance and genuine inability on the part of the users to cope with the system. One memorable example of this occurred in a large company planning to install an on-line information retrieval system; a rumor circulated among the male staff that the visual display unit terminals would make them sterile. Once established, no amount of training could overcome their prejudice. Less dramatic resistance will almost inevitably appear when almost any large-scale innovation is being planned.

REAL-TIME HARDWARE

There are three basic types of equipment required for any real-time system. The first is one or more main frame computers with the appropriate communications software, applications programs, and file management facilities for controlling processing. The second is communications equipment for the network of data transmission. The third is terminal equipment for input and output.

The transmission network may require telephone lines based on the public switched network supplied by the common carriers (for example, the telephone company, or in the United Kingdom the post office); or in-house or dedicated cables, or both. In addition, there will be requirements for modems, multiplexers, concentrators, communications controllers, and possibly front-end computers. All of these will be defined and explained in the next chapter.

Terminals can be visual display units, teleprinters, cash receipting machines, badge or credit card readers, digitizers, or even a minicomputer with a full set of standard input/output peripherals. More detail about these will also be given in the next chapter; the chapters following will discuss systems design considerations for the output for them.

Note that the boundaries between the categories of main computer, network, and terminals are not necessarily distinct in all areas. For example, certain communications controllers contain resident software; and some terminals are programmable or contain built-in communications equipment, or both.

CHAPTER 11

Data Transmission and Communications Hardware

The basic technical concepts around which a real-time system is built are introduced in this chapter. Under the general heading of data transmission, the subjects covered are lines and modes of transmission. Communications hardware covers line controllers, multiplexing, concentrators, and types of terminals. Finally, there is an outline of the functions of the software needed to support data transmission of this equipment.

DATA TRANSMISSION

Communication between remote terminals and a central computer is accomplished by data transmission. Data is sent in binary, that is, zero and one bits, over wire and cable. The growth of transmission of data in this way has been possible because the lines for sending it already exist: telephone and telegraph networks. A line over which Morse code or the human voice can be transmitted is entirely suitable for the relatively simple binary code. Other possible methods include satellite transmission, microwave, and cable television networks; but telephone and telegraph lines are the most important today, and we will concern ourselves only with these.

Telegraph Lines

The binary pattern is sent over a telegraph line by changes in the voltage on the line. The usual voltages are +80 volts for binary zero and −80 volts for binary one. For this and other transmission methods, speeds are measured in bits per second. Transmission speeds on telegraph lines usually do not exceed 100 bits per second (bps). Telegraph lines are susceptible to signal fading and distortion. As a general rule of thumb, the faster the rate of transmission, the more errors occur; therefore the lower the quality of the line, the slower must be the speed to keep error rates below an acceptable maximum. More will be said about error rates later.

Telephone Lines

On telephone lines different frequencies of alternating current are used to represent binary patterns. Speeds over ordinary telephone lines are usually in the order of 2400 to 4800 bps. Speeds over dedicated cables and microwave links can be much higher; most are in the range of 48,000 to 100,000 bps. Telephone lines for data transmission may be part of the public switched network or may be rented from the carrier for the customer's exclusive use.

The transmission of data over the public network operates in much the same way as making a telephone call. It is necessary first to establish the link between the originating point and the receiving point by dialing. This can be done either by the computer or with an ordinary telephone set that is used for voice communication. One advantage in using the public network is that there are many possible paths from one point to another, so that if there is a fault on the line, it is possible to hang up and dial again. Leased lines do not offer this flexibility and usually cannot be used for ordinary calls as well. On the other hand the quality of the transmission is apt to be better on a leased line because there is no competition from other subscribers.

International data transmission over the public network is also possible. The problems are greater here because of the widely varying quality of the telephone systems in different countries; for example, most of Germany's telephone system was destroyed in World War II and has since been replaced with modern equipment, but England did not suffer as severely and is still using lines that date back to the 1920s. Achieving the cooperation of a number of different national telephone companies can be difficult, too; in one project undertaken by the author, transmission from remote stations in Spain, Italy, and France to central computers in England and Germany was planned, but the Italian link had to be postponed indefinitely because of the propensity of the Italian telephone operators to interrupt the "conversation" to see if all was well.

Line Utilization

The quality of the line is not the only factor affecting speed of transmission. The upper limit is theoretically imposed by the slowest of the devices connected to the network, that is, the terminals. As an example, consider a line capable of transmitting at 1200 bps (540,000 characters per hour). An interactive visual display unit can send and receive 6000 characters per hour. It would thus seem that the line could support 90 terminals working continuously. (Techniques for transmitting a number of different messages over the same line simultaneously will be discussed later.) A line that is occupied in this way for more than 50 percent of the time, however, is usually impractical. First, about 10 percent must be added for transmission of control information, in addition to the message itself. Furthermore, the pattern of the messages is unlikely to be linear. There will be peak times during the day when more people want to use the terminals than at other times. Using lines that can handle the peak load all the time, when the peak actually occurs for only a small portion of the day, is very uneconomical. Even if there is no daily, weekly, or seasonal pattern, random distribution dictates that the volume of traffic will vary. In our example the practical upper limit for the number of terminals connected is 54. A large part of the systems analyst's job when designing such a system is in determining the break-even point for line utilization and speed.

Transmission Modes

The three modes of data transmission are illustrated in Figure 11.1. Any line can be used to provide transmission in one direction only; this is known as the "simplex mode." Transmission in both directions can be accomplished in two ways. The half-duplex mode allows transmission in either direction, but only one way at a time; between each transmission the line has to be "turned around." The other mode is full duplex with simultaneous two-way transmission. An ordinary telephone conversation can be thought of as being half duplex; if any communication is to take place, only one person can talk at a time. To achieve full duplex transmission over public lines it is necessary to have a double connection.

Channels

Although a telephone line is usually thought of as a physical link between two locations, in practice individual wires are able to carry up

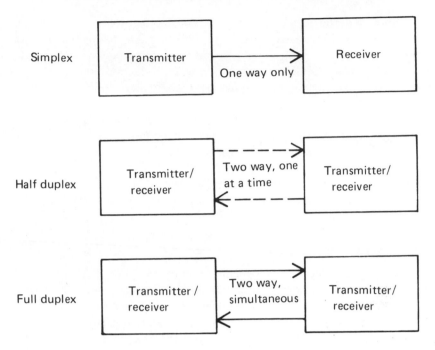

Fig. 11.1 Transmission modes

to 12 telephone conversations each. Users in areas where the telephone facilities are overstretched become aware of this when the telephone company attempts to cram too many conversations onto one wire. On a transatlantic conversation, for example, during peak hours when European and American business hours coincide, it is possible to hear "ghosts" of other conversations, or there are gaps in the transmission as the line is switched rapidly between different callers.

Each path on the wire is called a "channel." A channel is defined by two characteristics: its frequency range and its bandwidth.

Frequency. Frequency is measured in hertz (cycles per second; abbreviated Hz). The frequency range is the upper and lower limits of the frequency that the channel can transmit. Some examples follow.

 30 Hz–20 kHz: range detectable by the human ear
300 Hz–3.3 kHz: telephone range
 50 Hz–5   kHz: radio
 30 Hz–18 kHz: high-quality audio equipment

Note that the telephone range is much narrower than that detectable by the human ear; music played over the telephone always sounds tinny because both the upper and the lower frequencies are lost. Advances in modern stereo recording and reproduction equipment are now beyond the human range, making high-fidelity equipment at the upper end of the quality (and price) range irrelevant except to purists.

Bandwidth. The bandwidth is the difference between the lower and upper frequency limits, also expressed in hertz. For example, a line with a total bandwidth of 48 kHz can be divided into 12 channels of 4 kHz each. This is illustrated in Figure 11.2. A channel is allocated automatically by the exchange switching equipment when a connection over a public line is made; in the case of a private leased line it is permanently assigned.

Modulation

The public telegraph system, like computers, uses the absence or presence of a signal to represent a zero or one bit. The public telephone system, in contrast, is analog in operation; bits are represented by changes in the signal. A carrier signal (alternating current) is first set up between the transmitter and the receiver. The bit pattern is then superimposed on the carrier by changing or modulating the signal in one of three ways.

The three modulation techniques are amplitude modulation, frequency modulation, and phase modulation. They are illustrated in Figure 11.3. To change the digital bit pattern to a modulated representation and back again after transmission, a device called a "modulator-demodulator" is required. This is a "black box" attached to, or built into, each sending device and each receiving device. It is called a *modem.*

Asynchronous versus Synchronous Transmission

Asynchronous transmission does not require that the sending device and the receiving device be synchronized with each other before data transmission begins. The data is sent in discrete character groups, usually 10 or 11 bits each. The connection is made, and at the start the line is in an idle state called the "one state." A change (modulation) to the zero state is the start bit indicating to the receiver that a character will now be sent. The eight data bits are then transmitted by modulation—one of the three methods described above. This is illustrated in Figure 11.4. The line then returns to the idle one state for

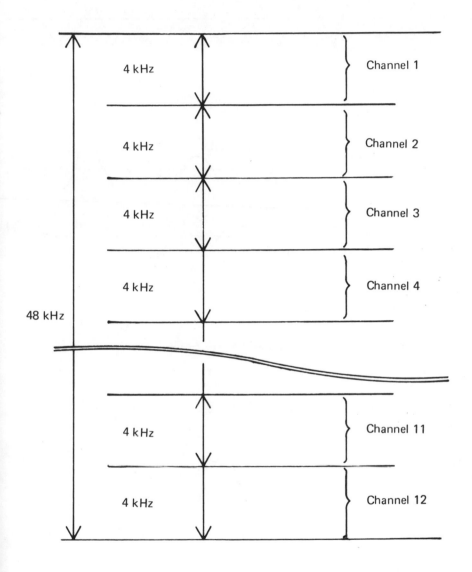

Fig. 11.2   Bandwidth allocation

Unmodulated carrier

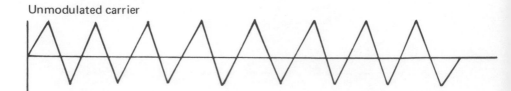

Amplitude modulation

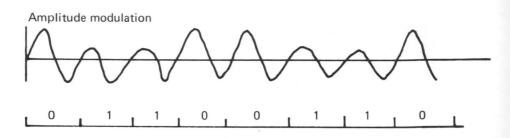

0   1   1   0   0   1   1   0

Frequency modulation

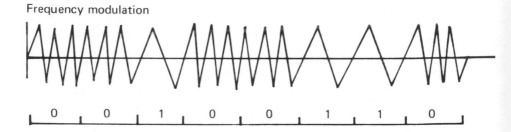

0   0   1   0   0   1   1   0

Phase modulation

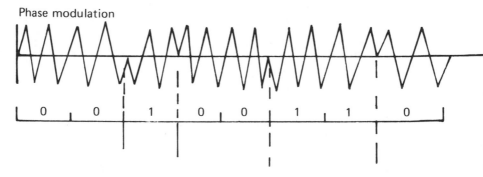

0   0   1   0   0   1   1   0

Fig. 11.3   Modulation techniques

134

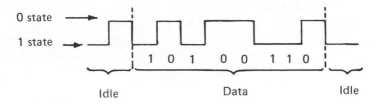

Fig. 11.4 Asynchronous transmission

1, 1.42, or 2 bit times before the start bit for the next character is generated. The actual timing depends on the device and the transmission code. Use of the start and stop signals are called "framing" the character.

Figure 11.5 shows synchronous transmission. Blocks of data are

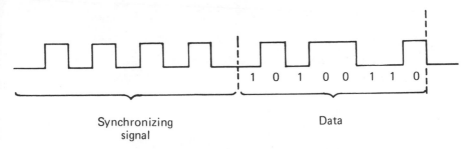

Fig. 11.5 Synchronous transmission

sent in a continuous stream without framing. To do this it is necessary to synchronize the sending device and the receiving device before data transmission begins. This is achieved either by transmitting a continuous special bit pattern before and after each block of data or by transmitting a number of patterns just prior to the data. In the example in the illustration the idle line carries a synchronizing signal of alternate zero and one bits; and deviation from this will be recognized by the receiver as data characters.

Asynchronous transmission is the less complex of the two methods and is usually used for slower electromechanical devices such as keyboard printers and teleprinters; transmission speeds for these types of terminals tend to be less than 300 bps. It is also used for medium-speed devices (300 to 5000 bps) like remote unbuffered paper tape readers and punches, card readers, and line printers. The reason for this, in addition to the lack of a need for special timing equipment, is that asynchronous transmission is susceptible to distortion and therefore error rates would be too great at higher speeds. The receiving device depends entirely on the incoming signal; any distortion in it will cause an error. Note also that for every 8-bit character, 11 bits must be transmitted, so asynchronous transmission is relatively inefficient.

Synchronous transmission, on the other hand, requires that the transmitter and the receiver be locked together on a common timing source provided by the line. There is thus less sensitivity to distortion, although a faulty beginning can mean that the entire message is garbled. Transmission is also faster because of the "burst" mode with no bits lost for synchronization. It is also more expensive because of the more sophisticated equipment required, and because line costs are higher. It is used for buffered visual display units, card readers, and line printers in the 300 to 5000 bps range, and for intercomputer communications at higher speeds.

Baud

Baud is the measure of transmission speed. Baud refers to the number of times the condition (modulation) of the carrier line changes in 1 second. Because most transmission is two-state transmission, that is, zero or one (see Figure 11.6), baud is usually taken to mean bits per second. This is not strictly correct, however. Other modes of transmission are possible, as in Figure 11.7. This is four-state transmission and it is possible to send two bits at a time (dibits). The bits-per-second rate is thus twice that of the baud.

Data Transmission Errors

References have been made in the discussion above to transmission errors, and the rule of thumb given was that the more error prone the line, the slower must be the transmission for an acceptable level of accuracy.

Errors, or dropouts, are caused by thermal noise, cross talk, ghosting or pickup from other circuits, and impulse interference. As was pointed out above, the probability of any of these occurring depends on the type of line and the type of connection. It is always necessary to include in the system some means of checking the transmission and correcting transmission errors. Methods of doing this are by timing checks, parity checks, and block character counts.

Significant improvements are being made by the common carriers to reduce error rates. Most public telephone systems have a high degree

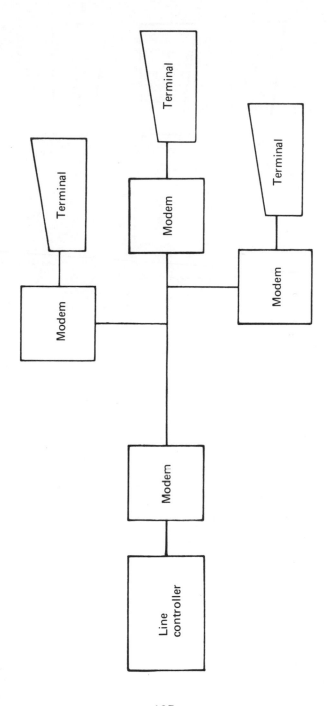

Fig. 11.6 Multidrop line

137

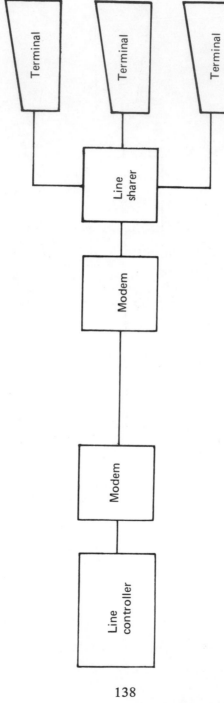

Fig. 11.7　Shared Line

138

of reliability in any case, having been built for long life and low maintenance. If a public line is too noisy, it is always possible to hang up and
dial again. Distance seems to have little effect on error rates because
most noise is introduced within 20 miles of the connection point by
switching equipment in the local exchange. Because the noise level increases with the level of traffic, the users who have the most difficulty
are those in areas where the telephone company has underestimated demand. Leased lines bypass the local exchanges and are thus more accurate, but if a fault on the line does occur, there is no alternative method
of transmission unless an advance contingency arrangement has been
made.

Error rates range from 1 in every 10,000 bits transmitted to 1 in
every 10,000,000 or better. The average for the United States is about 1
in 100,000 and for the United Kingdom about 1 in 20,000 over public
lines. Leased line circuits have lower error rates, and most common
carriers will guarantee that the rate will not go above a specified maximum level.

COMMUNICATIONS HARDWARE

Communications hardware can be roughly divided into the two
categories of control equipment and terminals. The first category includes line controllers, multiplexors, and concentrators. The category of
terminals comprises teleprinters, visual display units, remote peripherals,
and special purpose devices such as banking terminals and badge and
credit card readers. Much terminal equipment is designed to order for a
specific purpose. In this section the functions of these major items of
hardware will be described.

Line Controllers

There are two types of line controllers: single-channel controllers
for transmission over one line between one sending device and one receiving device, and multichannel controllers for systems with more than
one independent line. The controller carries out all the essential functions of data transmission over a line or channel. These are as follows:

1. Parallel to serial bit conversion
2. Assembly and disassembly of characters
3. Synchronization

4. Parity generation and checking
5. Control character generation and checking
6. Interrupt and interface control

The controller is in turn driven by software that is in the main computer to accomplish functions such as buffering of messages and error processing and logging.

Multiplexors

Multiplexing is a technique developed to take advantage of the high transmission speeds of communications lines as opposed to the relatively low sending and receiving rates of some terminals. A number of such slow terminals can be connected to one fast line. A communications network having many terminals connected by an equal number of lines would be expensive. There are two versions of this technique: frequency division multiplexing and time division multiplexing.

Frequency Division Multiplexing. Frequency division multiplexing (FDM) functions by splitting the line into a number of smaller bandwidth channels, which is done by a small hardware device. This multiplexing is used only for asynchronous processing and is susceptible to transmission noise because of the resulting small bandwidths. It is therefore used only for a small number of low-speed terminals.

Time Division Multiplexing. Time division multiplexing (TDM) is accomplished by interleaving transmissions to and from different terminals on the same line. The multiplexor scans all terminals that are on-line and allocates a line time slot equivalent to one character. This slot is used to transmit a character if there is one; if not, a null code is transmitted. Sometimes the scanning operation is performed by the communications processor instead, in which case the multiplexor is said to be transparent. Time division multiplexing is used for both asynchronous and synchronous transmission, with each "subchannel" using the entire bandwidth.

Note that in either type of multiplexing, demultiplexing must be done at the other end.

Each terminal sharing the line has a unique wired address. The multiplexor scans each in turn to give it an opportunity to send or be sent to. This is called "polling." Messages to and from a terminal always carry that terminal's address as part of the message, so a two-way conversation can be carried out without confusion or interference from other terminals on the line. There are two basic configuration patterns for this type of system: multidrop and sharing.

Multidrop Lines. Multidrop lines have several terminals connected to a single line, each with its own modem (modulator-demodulator, as explained earlier). This is illustrated in Figure 11.6. This can be thought of as a "party line" system. The message being transmitted goes to each terminal in turn; if the address does not match, it is sent on to the next. An alternate method is to send the same message to each terminal with the message being ignored by all but the one it is intended for.

Line Sharing. Line sharing is illustrated in Figure 11.7. The terminals can be thought of as extension telephones sharing the same number, but with one difference: A message is addressed to a particular terminal. It may go directly to that one and that one only, or it may go to all of them and be ignored if the addresses do not match, depending on the characteristics of the communications equipment used.

Concentrators

Multiplexors effectively convert a number of low-speed transmissions into one high-speed transmission. Concentrators further improve the efficiency of the network by converting asynchronous transmissions to high-speed synchronous ones. The concentrator is often a programmable minicomputer, called a "front-end" processor. This allows validation and message editing to be performed before onward transmission to the central computer. A configuration incorporating a front-end processor is shown in Figure 11.8.

TERMINALS

There is a wide range of data processing equipment that can be attached to a communications network as terminals. This section gives an overview of the various categories. More detail will be given about the two most widely used types—visual display units and teleprinters—in the next two chapters, where design considerations for output are also given.

Remote Data Terminals

Included in this category are the standard computer peripherals that are sited at locations geographically separate from the main computer, whether in the next room or halfway around the world, but remaining under its direct control. A control unit provides the interface

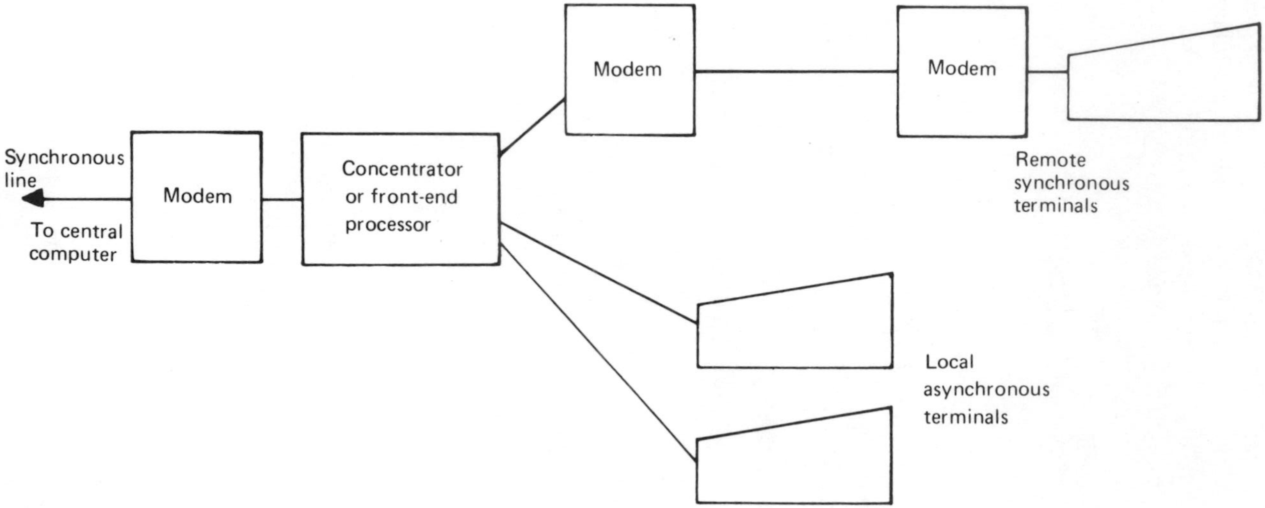

Fig. 11.8 Front-end processing

Remote synchronous terminals

Modem

Modem

Local asynchronous terminals

Concentrator or front-end processor

Modem

Synchronous line

To central computer

between the peripheral and the telephone line. The control unit may simply act as a multiplexor or it may be a small programmable front-end processor. In the latter case local batch processing can be carried on as well.

An example configuration is shown in Figure 11.9. Such an arrangement might exist in, say, a company branch office not large enough to justify a full, independent, data processing service on the site. Data preparation facilities are available here, however—in this case card punching. Batches of cards are prepared in the usual way. At a pre-scheduled time, possibly at night when line charges are lower and noise on the telephone lines is less, the remote card reader is connected to the central computer. The connection can be initiated from either end by a human operator dialing the appropriate number. The central computer would then activate the card reader (which was previously loaded and made ready) and cause the cards to be read and the data to be transmitted. The action required in the case of a transmission fault or other problem, such as a jam in the card reader, depends on the sophistication of the control equipment. In some cases the card image would be buffered at the card reader, and after reception at the main computer it would be sent back down the line to verify the accuracy of the message. Any discrepancy would cause a retransmission. In other cases any interruption would require a restart of the job from the beginning. Management reports for the branch office would be transmitted to the line printer by the central computer in a similar way. The teleprinter, a slower device, would be used for control messages and low-volume output. Typical operating speeds for a configuration like the one in the illustration are shown in the table below.

| | Line Speed | | |
	1200 bps	2400 bps	4800 bps
80 character line printer	76 lpm	173 lpm	326 lpm
132 character line printer	46 lpm	105 lpm	198 lpm
40 column card reader	135 cpm	270 cpm	320 cpm
80 column card reader	85 cpm	170 cpm	320 cpm

Teleprinters

A teleprinter is hard-copy character (as opposed to line) printer. It can be used for passive transmission—that is, messages from the central computer only—or for interactive transmission, which is two-way

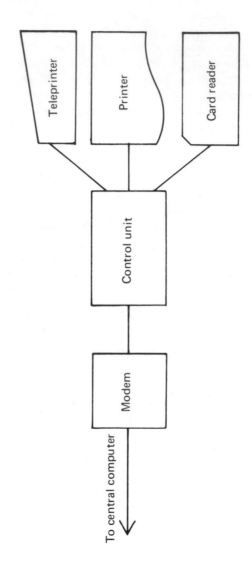

Fig. 11.9 Remote data input/output

144

communication. Input can be via either the keyboard, similar to a type-writer keyboard, or paper tape. Output is printed hard-copy alphanumeric data. Teleprinters are often used for remote input and for control messages between the computer and the remote station. More detail about these devices and about designing input and output message formats will be given in Chapter 12.

Visual Display Units

A visual display unit (VDU) is a televisionlike cathode-ray tube. Display, controlled by the central computer, can be alphanumeric or graphic, or both. Visual display units can be used in a passive mode for output only, or in an interactive mode with input from the user being either through keyboard or a light pen. These units will be described in more detail in Chapter 13.

Intelligent Terminals

An intelligent terminal is one that has its own programmable memory, thus giving it a certain amount of processing power. Programs for input validation, for example, can be loaded into the terminal's memory via cassette tape or disk. The memory also contains instructions for control procedures for transmission. An intelligent configuration based on a Burroughs TC500 memory unit is shown in Figure 11.10. The TC500 incorporates an alphanumeric keyboard and function keys to call stored programs from disk into memory and to control the peripherals.

Data Collection Terminals

Data collection or data gathering devices are remote peripherals for input of data in either a batch or an on-line mode. These can be teleprinters, badge readers, punched card readers, credit card readers, optical wand readers, or other special purpose devices. Card and badge readers often include a small numeric keyboard or thumb dials for input of variable information associated with the badge or card—for example, time of day or codes. They allow input to be made directly from areas where environmental conditions would be unsuitable for other types of equipment, as for example, from the factory floor. Most are very slow devices, and so a large number can be attached to one line. A very limited amount of information can be sent to the human operator of the device from the central computer, often consisting, for example, of a "go-ahead" light to indicate that transmission may begin or that the credit card inserted in the reader is a valid one.

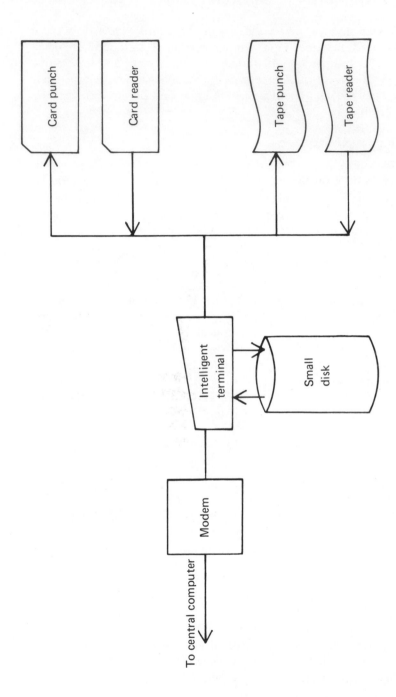

Fig. 11.10 Intelligent remote configuration

Data capture at the other end can be by the main computer on-line, but is more often by some other peripheral such as a paper tape punch, magnetic tape drive, or card punch. The input data is then processed in a batch mode. Applications include clocking in of store and factory workers to provide payroll data; job progressing in a machine shop or factory; cash dispensing in a bank; and collection of sales data on the selling floor of a department store.

Because these terminals are input rather than output devices, no more will be said about them here. Details of hardware and example applications will be found in Wooldridge, 1973a in the Bibliography.

COMMUNICATIONS SOFTWARE

Conventional batch programs running in third generation computers make extensive use of software dedicated to handling the complex tasks of file management, input/output, device error recovery, and operator communication. On-line systems introduce further complexities in all of these areas. Furthermore, some controlling interface between the communications user programs and the terminal network is required.

The functional requirements for communications software can be summarized as follows:

1. Assembly of bits into characters and characters into messages and the reverse
2. Translation from computer machine code into line transmission code and the reverse
3. Initiation and control of input/output on communications devices and allocation and reallocation of terminals
4. Message routing to terminals and polling or scanning
5. Provision of temporary storage areas for data being transmitted to, or received from, remote terminals and maintenance of queues of messages awaiting processing or transmission
6. Identification, analysis, logging, reporting, and correction of errors
7. Logging and reporting terminal and line usage statistics

Items one and two above may, however, be carried out by the hardware.

SUMMARY

The objective of this chapter has been to provide readers who have had no previous real-time experience with a basic working knowledge of the principles of data communications in preparation for the more detailed treatment of on-line output that follows. It is not possible to give guidelines for designing a full-scale real-time network within the scope of this book; practical training in addition to study is essential before undertaking such a project, in any case. In that this chapter has been a parenthetical aside, as in a Victorian novel, we now return to our main plot.

CHAPTER 12

Teleprinter Message Design

This chapter covers the characteristics and uses of teleprinters and the considerations for designing "man-machine dialogue," the message pairs that are necessary for interactive communication between the user at the terminal and the system resident in the CPU at the main computer. In this sense the discussion includes input as well as output. The other major use of a teleprinter is as an input device for fairly high-volume data being entered into the computer system from a remote location; and even though this is not within the scope of this book, some possibilities for increasing the efficiency of that type of input will also be included in the discussion.

TELEPRINTER CHARACTERISTICS

Teleprinters (also called teletypewriters, telecommunications printers, and so on) are typewriterlike devices connected to the main computer as explained in the last chapter. They are character printers using continuous stationery like the console typewriter in the computer room. The keyboard has a standard QWERT layout with additional keys for control symbols and special characters, but it differs from the ordinary typewriter in that there are upper-case letters only. There is a shift key so that some keys have two symbols. The platen width is usually 72 or 80 characters. The stationery is fed by friction as in a typewriter or by pins like the high-speed printer, depending on the model of the device. There is a split-platen model available so that two different types of continuous stationery can be used in the same teleprinter at the same time.

149

Teleprinters are often operated as unbuffered, asynchronous devices. The speeds are low, in the range of 10 to 120 cps when printing output, and limited by the skill of the operator when input is being entered. With an unbuffered device, input from the keyboard is transmitted to the central computer one character at a time as it is entered. With a buffer as part of the electronics of the device, an entire line is entered into the buffer and transmitted when the operator keys a special transmit code at the end of the line or when there is a carriage return for the next line.

A hard copy of all messages is created. Some devices print the input as it is entered, with keys or a ball typing head. In others there is one circuit connecting the keyboard to the central computer and another from the computer back to the printing unit. As characters are keyed in they are transmitted and the parity or other controls are checked; each character is then immediately transmitted back for printing.

Some teleprinters are passive and can only receive, producing a hard copy. These are usually used for messages of relatively low to medium volume from the central computer to the remote station. They have no keyboard. Others can be used in the interactive mode, both sending and receiving. When the device is in the receive mode, the computer sends a signal that first locks the keyboard so that the operator cannot overwrite the message being sent. This type is often used for input and for retrieval of information from files at the central computer, again usually of low to medium volume.

It is possible to attach to the teleprinter a paper tape punch, a paper tape reader, a card punch, a card reader, a cassette disk or tape, or some combination of these. One such remote station is shown in the photograph in Figure 12.1. This is the Univac DCT 1000 buffered printer terminal. A card punch and a card reader can also be seen; alternatively, a paper tape reader punch could be attached. On the far right is a visual display unit with keyboard; this type of device will be covered in the next chapter.

Teleprinters as terminals are indicated in situations in which the volume of input/output is not relatively high, and where there is a necessity for a hard copy of transactions. The model chosen will depend also on the local environment in which it will be used, and the cost, the speed, and the complexity of the input. If a supplier other than the computer manufacturer is chosen, it will be necessary to investigate hardware and software compatibility; fault diagnosis, repair, and maintenance service available; and any special features required of the machine.

Another major consideration is the skill of the operators. This can

Fig. 12.1 Remote data station (Courtesy Sperry Univac)

vary from very good in a full-time data entry job to poor where the terminal is used on an occasional basis by an operator whose primary job is something else. As a general guide a trained operator can be expected to put in an effective day of about 5½ hours. Unless other figures are available from previous experience, the keying rate should be assumed to be not more than 10,000 key depressions per hour (kdph) for numeric work, and not more than 5000 key depressions per hour for alphabetic or mixed data. A casual operator whose main job responsibility is other than terminal operation should be assumed to have a keying rate not greater than 3600 depressions per hour, alphanumeric. For hunt-and-peck typists and especially in early stages of implementation this rate could be much lower.

Output speed will, of course, depend on the rated speed of the device and the characteristics of the network of which it is a part. In an interactive environment with alternate input from the operator and output from the computer, a further factor that must be considered is that of delay in response. Irritation and frustration of the user increase dramatically when the response delay is between 5 and 10 seconds. This levels out and then decreases as the delay approaches 30 seconds, until, presumably, the operator loses interest altogether and walks away. In an on-line system the rule of thumb is to aim for a response delay on output of not more than 5 seconds.

INTERACTIVE DIALOGUE

The design exercise for communications between the operator at the terminal and the central computer system consists of specifying all the different types of messages that can occur. In even a simple system the number of these will turn out to be quite high.

Messages can be thought of as always occurring in pairs. Within the pair the first half is always initiated by the computer system even if this is only an acknowledgment that the system is now ready to accept input. The end of the transaction will also always be by the computer system, acknowledging acceptance. An illustration of the basic types of message pairs is shown in Figure 12.2. The system first acknowledges that it is ready to accept a message in. The operator then keys it, and

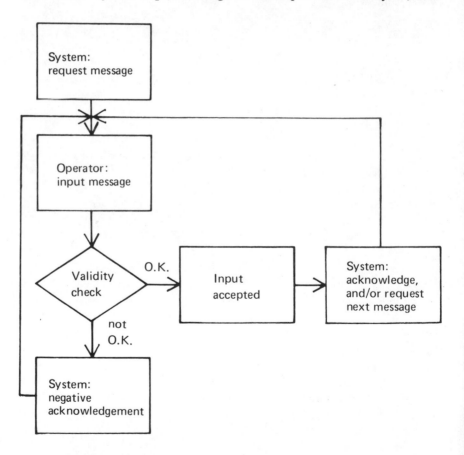

Fig. 12.2   Message pairs

basic editing and validity checks are performed. If an error is detected, the operator is informed by the system and retries. If not, the system acknowledges, perhaps by asking for another input message.

There are certain basic design criteria that messages of this type should satisfy. These are summarized in Figure 12.3. First, there is the

---

Identification

Brevity
    preprinted stationery
    tabulation and form feed
    codes

Field separation
    spacing
    special characters
    fixed-length fields
    preprinted stationery

Error correction
    reinput
    cancel character, field or line
    negative input message

Acknowledgment of Successful Transaction

Fig. 12.3   Message design criteria

need for some kind of identification before a message pair begins, especially for input. Both input and output should be brief to keep keying and transmission time to a minimum. Some method or methods of field separation must be decided on. There must be error detection and correction routines; these can account for a large proportion of the system logic design. Finally, there must be acknowledgment to the operator of successful completion of a message pair. As was pointed out above this can be combined with the system acknowledgment initiating the next message pair.

Identification of the input to follow is always important but becomes more and more complicated as the number of different types of input messages increases. A code or key word, not too long, is needed. When a series of items is being entered, there is often a logical seqeunce, so that once the type of input has been identified what follows can be deduced by the system by implication.

All messages should be as brief as is consistent with clarity. The use of preprinted stationery can greatly assist with this aim. It eliminates the need for the output of standard titles and column headings and allows fields to be printed out closer together, thus doing away with the need to transmit spaces. The teleprinter can be advanced to predetermined tabulation stops automatically, and forms can be similarly turned up for starting a new page once they are positioned for the day's transmission.

Field separation is necessary both in the input and in the output mode. There are a number of ways of doing this, and various ones may be intermixed in the same system for different types of messages or fields. Spacing is an obvious solution, particularly for data consisting of fixed-length fields, and for output from the system to the operator. Free-form input requires some kind of special character as a field separator because spaces or blanks may be valid input with another meaning. If preprinted stationery aligned with tab stops is used, as mentioned above, however, the system may be able to recognize the position of the entry by virtue of a special message character automatically transmitted when the operator tabs.

One of the major advantages of an on-line system over a batch system is that detection and correction of errors can be done immediately. There are two types of errors that need to be considered: those that are conscious and recognized by the operator before the message is finished and unconscious errors detected by the system after transmission is complete. Editing criteria and the types of checks that can be applied for the latter type were covered in detail in Chapter 6. With an on-line system it may be necessary to divide editing routines into basic ones for immediate use and finer checking after the input has been accumulated for processing. This is because of memory and input/output time limitations if a number of different edit routines need to be resident in memory along with a variety of message processing programs.

Errors of which the operator becomes aware before final transmission of the message can be corrected by him at once. Facilities are usually needed for character correction when the incorrect character is noticed before any others are keyed; this is also true for field correction, for line cancellation when the whole line is wrong or when subsequent characters have been keyed, and for message cancellation. Such corrections can be accomplished by the back-space key on the teleprinter, which, when used automatically, cancels as many characters as the number of times the key is depressed working backward from the last one entered; or a special character can be entered by the operator to signal cancellation. An example of this is shown in Figure 12.4. Two special characters have been arbitrarily chosen as cancella-

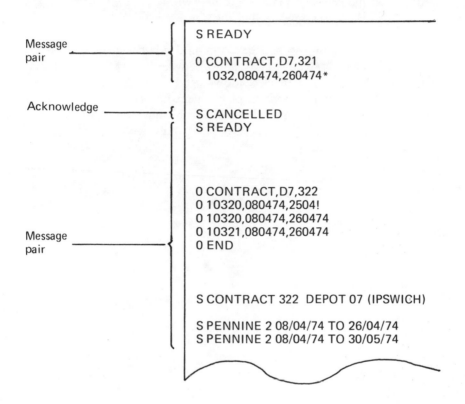

Message pair

Acknowledge

Message pair

```
S READY

0 CONTRACT,D7,321
  1032,080474,260474*

S CANCELLED
S READY


0 CONTRACT,D7,322
0 10320,080474,2504!
0 10320,080474,260474
0 10321,080474,260474
0 END


S CONTRACT 322  DEPOT 07 (IPSWICH)

S PENNINE 2 08/04/74 TO 26/04/74
S PENNINE 2 08/04/74 TO 30/05/74
```

0 = operator
S = system
* = cancel message
! = cancel line

Fig. 12.4   Error correction and dialogue

tion characters for the illustration. An asterisk cancels an entire message and an exclamation point cancels a line. The system will acknowledge the cancellation of a message. In the first message pair the operator noticed that the contract number 321 was wrong only after starting the second line. He therefore cancelled the entire message with an asterisk, the system acknowledged, and he started again. This time he miskeyed the last number of the second line, but noticed the error after a few more characters were entered. He cancelled the line with an exclamation mark; the system in effect acknowledged by returning the carriage for him to the beginning position of the next line and the operator re-entered it. The operator signaled the end of his half of the message pair by entering END, and the system began to reply with the information that had been requested.

CHAPTER 13

Visual Display Unit Design

Visual display units (VDU) are usually more expensive than teleprinters both in terms of hardware costs and of system complexity and implementation costs, but a system built around them offers many advantages over teleprinters or other on-line terminals. This assumes, of course, that the justification for a real-time system exists in the first place. The major advantage of a visual display unit is the factor of fast transmission and display of information for human use. For an input-oriented system, this means rapid editing of the data and error correction at the source. Options for formatting are much more extensive, too, up to and including the interactive display of complex graphical data. The only functional advantage of teleprinters over visual display units is the hard copy they provide, but there are several ways of obtaining a hard copy of the screen display on a display unit, as will be discussed later.

Applications for visual display unit based on-line systems fall into the three general categories: scientific and engineering systems, on-line data entry, and inquiry and control systems. Examples of the first are engineering design and structural analysis. On-line data entry has been mentioned in several contexts in earlier chapters, and can be thought of as being the "bread and butter" of on-line systems. An inquiry and control system may be an extension of data entry, in that it is first necessary to get the information onto the files before it can be retrieved and manipulated. Examples of this type of system range from automated control of manufacturing processes to a clerical lookup in response to a customer's query. More advanced applications extend into the area of management information systems, with the visual display units used for retrieval of business information, and interactive modeling and projections. More specific examples of applications and displays will be given throughout this chapter.

The design of a visual display based system begins with and is inextricably interwoven with hardware and software selection, particularly the choice of the display terminals themselves. The visual display unit market is a rapidly expanding one, and there is a wide choice of manufacturers and of options on any given model. Rather than presenting a description of hardware features followed by a discussion of design criteria, therefore, a somewhat different approach is taken here. After an outline of the general technology on which these units are based, a number of the more useful and popular hardware/software options will be described along with the system possibilities each one offers.

VISUAL DISPLAY UNITS

The major components of a typical visual display unit configuration are shown in Figure 13.1. The display itself is a cathode-ray tube,

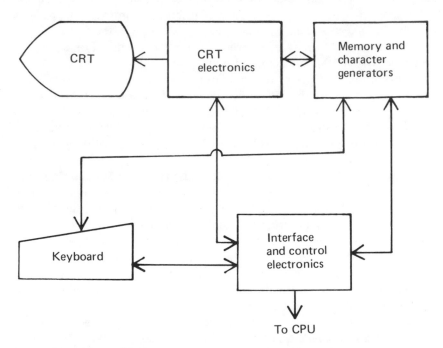

Fig. 13.1 Visual display unit and keyboard configuration

often described as being like a television screen. The keyboard may be a separate unit, but is often an integral part of the unit along with the cathode-ray tube screen. Various control components link the elements together and provide the interface with the network leading to the central computer.

The screen is coated with phosphor on the back. An electron gun "shoots" electrons at the back of the screen, creating a glow where they hit. The stream of electrons can be controlled to produce whatever images are desired. This is a transitory effect, however, and to create a stable image that will last long enough to be seen and studied by a human being, it is necessary to repeat the firing of the electrons for as long as the image is to remain on the screen. This is called "refreshing" the display. It must be done between 30 and 50 times a second to avoid a visible flicker.

Refresh Methods

There are several different ways to refresh the image. The stream of data that creates the image in the first place comes from the central computer. The computer can continue to send the same information to the visual display unit until some instruction reaches it to stop or to update the image. This method obviously is expensive of computer time and memory and requires 10 to 30 times as much traffic on the transmission lines than some other method would. An alternative is to transmit the control information to the display unit once, store it in a memory locally, and refresh from there until a new command is received. Intelligent terminals make this entirely feasible and usually preferable. Newer models use a memory the size of a pinhead for refreshing. The electronics of the visual display unit are more complex, but the savings in computer time and channel usage often overbalance this. A third method, used in some models, is called the "direct-view bistable storage tube" (DVBST). In addition to the usual stream of focused high-speed electrons to trace out the desired image, there is a second electron gun continuously firing low-speed electrons over the entire screen. This has a balancing effect sufficient to maintain the original image until some change is signaled. The direct-view bistable storage tube does away with both local control units and the necessity for refreshing from the central computer. Note that in either case, however, it is still necessary for a record of the original image to be maintained at the central computer, so that inquiries or updating can be handled with reference to it.

The Keyboard

A keyboard associated with the visual display unit provides a method for entering input into the central computer system and for controlling the display and calling for information to be displayed on it. An example of such a unit and a typical keyboard is shown in Figure 13.2.

Fig. 13.2   Visual display unit and keyboard (Courtesy Data 100 Systems)

As can be seen in Figure 13.2 there is a standard complement of typewriterlike QWERT keys and numeric keys. A shift gives a second control meaning to some of these keys. In addition there is a numeric pad on the right for entering high-volume numeric-only data, which is done with one hand instead of with two as on a typewriter. The pad of keys on the far right contains function keys for controlling the image; examples of these will be discussed later. Visual display unit keyboards are entirely electronic; some models have an adjustable audible key click.

ALPHANUMERIC VS GRAPHIC VISUAL DISPLAY UNITS

All visual display units have an alphanumeric display capability; some are also suitable for graphic displays. Some graphic display terminals are purpose built, others are alphanumeric terminals with graphics as an optional hardware/software feature that can be added on.

Character Generation

There are a number of different methods of generating characters onto the face of the visual display unit screen. The three principal ones are shaped beam, dot vector, and raster scan. The shaped-beam method is similar to that used in Charactron computer output microfilm character generation, with the electron beam being shone through a template to project the desired character. With the dot-vector method, the electron beam moves to draw the characters on the screen as a series of predefined segments. The raster scan technique is similar to that of the home television image creation, and as such is particularly suitable for graphics.

Character Set and Size

General-purpose visual display units offer a standard character set. The viewing area of the screen of an alphanumeric terminal is defined by its size and by the number of characters that can be displayed at one time. Typical sizes are in the range of 4 by 6 inches to 8 by 10 inches. Special-purpose high-capacity screens are also made; one familiar example is the wall-sized control screen at NASA spacecraft command center.

On a desk-top visual display unit the number of character positions of the display may range between 500 and 2000, depending on the size of the screen and on the size of the characters. A choice of four different character sizes that can be displayed at any one time is typical, but two sizes are adequate for most applications. An illustration showing different sizes and shapes of characters will be found in Figure 13.3. Note that characters can be combined for a crosshatch effect and also in this example that the alphabetics are in both upper and lower case.

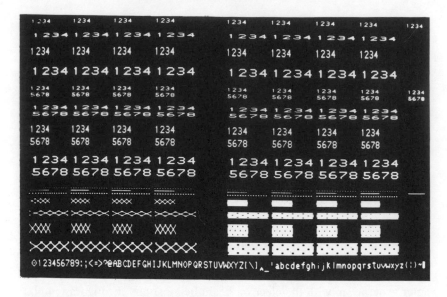

Fig. 13.3 Variable character sizes (Courtesy Data Disc, Inc.)

Variable character sizes give flexibility for titling and headings of displays, for labels on graphic displays, and for drawing the viewer's attention to selected areas. On the other hand, in a formatted display such as might be used for data entry, variable character sizes could introduce unnecessary difficulties in the spacing of data items.

In graphics systems the capacity of the screen is defined by the number of addressable points. Typical arrays would be 512 by 512, or 640 by 480. This density gives enough points so that lines and curves made up of a large number of points are seen as continuous lines or solid patches.

Two displays showing a typical mix of alphanumeric and graphical symbols are shown in Figures 13.4 and 13.5.

DISPLAY MODES

There are three principal modes of display on a visual display unit screen: scrolling, paging, and framing.

Scrolling.   Scrolling is similar to the output of a printer or tele-printer. The output, or the input as it is entered from the keyboard, is displayed with a minimum of formatting. The screen is used as if it

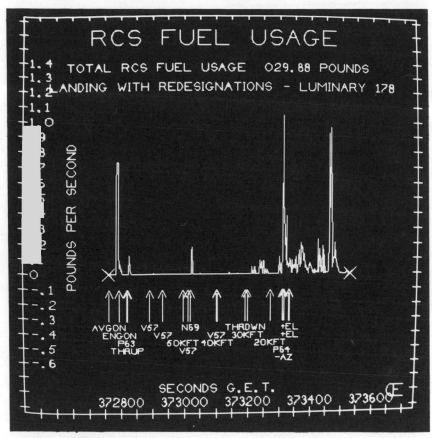

Fig. 13.4 Example of display (Courtesy Data Disc, Inc.)

were a continuous roll of paper, with the top, or oldest, line disappearing from the screen as the newest appears at the bottom, all intervening lines moving up one position. The display illustrated in Figure 13.6 is of this type.

Paging. Paging is a technique used mainly in inquiry systems. It allows the operator to display a page of file information and then select the next display. (Methods of selection will be described later.) The first page disappears entirely from the screen to be replaced with a new page of information. An example is a personnel records system, in which input from the operator via the keyboard requests information on all engineering apprentices. A list of names is displayed, and the operator can then request to see more detailed records of certain individuals.

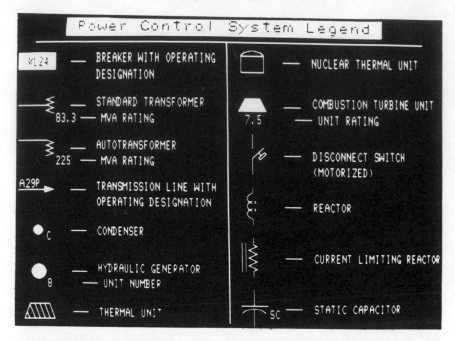

Fig. 13.5   **Example of display** (Courtesy Data Disc, Inc.)

Framing.   Framing is usually associated with data entry systems. The screen displays a facsimile of the source document from which the operator is working, or a facsimile of a source document on which data might be written, perhaps as the operator collects information from a telephone caller. Space is left within the display for the variable information. The frame can be transmitted from the computer, or it can be held on local storage, such as cassette disk or tape. Such a system will usually have local editing and validation facilities as well. Only the variable information, not the frame, need be transmitted to the central computer. As the operator keys in the information, it appears on the appropriate space on the screen. Errors can be corrected immediately. There are a number of different ways of highlighting or selecting areas of the display for the operator's attention, including different intensities, blinking, and the use of a cursor. These will be described below.

     There are a number of important input and output options that the systems designer can take advantage of to improve the legibility and usefulness of the visual display unit. A representative range, including all of the most popular ones, will be discussed here. They are as follows:

REAL TIME CORE DUMP

```
05600   005527  000000  073700  000000  000000  063700  164000  017670
05610   000000  017670  077701  017670  077702  017670  077703  017670
05620   077704  017670  000000  006020  127600  000000  002004  000000
05630   006003  027606  000000  007004  077667  073666  000000  000000
05640   063666  164000  047701  077701  017670  047702  077702  017670
05650   047703  077703  017670  047704  077704  017670  000000  000000
05660   037667  027561  000000  027623  000000  000000  005717  000000
05670   005656  000000  114075  000000  002004  164000  127670  000000


05700   005710  012701  014710  001010  000351  000000  000000  000000
05710   001441  024000  012040  014100  000540  000711  000070  000012
05720   000007  000003  177774  100000  000007  177775  000002  177775
05730   100000  004460  000000  000010  000010  177774  177774  000000
05740   070000  070000  012370  014450  002444  004614  000005  000010
05750   000010  177774  177774  170000  000000  070307  060304  040224
05760   070304  060303  040226  050320  040224  070303  015653  027714
05770   006206  006047  006047  006047  006047  006210  006213  006221


06000   001401  024000  012100  014400  002200  004600  012100  014400
06010   006300  012024  014400  006400  012100  014400  006500  012500
06020   014640  002140  004240  012500  014640  002300  004400  012500
06030   014640  002440  004540  012500  014640  002600  004700  012400
06040   014440  006540  016440  002540  004640  012440  014500  006640
06050   012400  014440  006440  016440  002440  004500  012440  014500
06060   006500  012400  014500  006340  012400  014440  006240  016440
06070   002200  004240  012440  014500  006200  012664  014740  006170


06100   016664  002170  004200  012664  014700  006200  016700  002200
06110   004224  012700  014740  006224  016740  002170  004224  001230
06120   012100  002750  000104  000111  000123  000120  000114  000101
06130   000131  000040  000115  000105  000123  000123  000101  000107
06140   000105  000040  000123  000127  000111  000124  000103  000110
06150   012100  002724  000127  000111  000124  000110  000040  000124
06160   000110  000105  000040  000115  000101  000111  000116  000040
06170   000103  000117  000115  000120  000125  000124  000105  001401
```

Fig. 13.6 Scroll-type display (Courtesy Data Disc, Inc.)

165

cursor	blinking
light pen	animation
rolling ball	reverse field
Rand tablet	halftone and color
intensity control	hard-copy output

Cursor

A cursor or trackball is a moving spot or symbol controlled by the visual display unit or by the software in the main computer. The cursor shows the next position to be entered on the screen. It is a simple but effective device, virtually indispensable for data entry and information retrieval applications.

The uses of the cursor are illustrated in Figures 13.7 and 13.8, where the cursor is represented by an equal sign. Figure 13.7 shows a data entry example. At the top a simple format has been displayed by the system for entry of details of movements of plant hire vehicles. The parentheses show where variable data fields are to be inserted. At the start the cursor is positioned at the first field. The bottom frame shows the appearance of the screen after all details for this contract have been keyed. The operator has entered the contract number, machine numbers, and movement dates. The last field is an end-of-record indicator, E. The next step on the part of the operator is to depress the transmit key, causing all the data in parentheses to be transmitted up to the new cursor position. The frame will then revert to its first format for the next contract.

Note that the data for transmission is *not* "read" from the screen; the display is purely for the benefit of the operator. As each character is keyed, it enters a storage buffer to await transmission. If the operator makes a conscious error, it can be corrected by the use of an erase key or by backspacing and rekeying at any time up until the transmit key is activated. The visual display unit must therefore have a buffer big enough to accommodate a full frame of data.

The example in Figure 13.8 shows the use of the cursor in an information retrieval example. The application area is plant hire, as above. The top frame shows the enquiry just before it is transmitted for processing. The operator has requested details of three machines, and the cursor is positioned at the end-of-record marker. If no E was entered, the system would assume that more data was coming and would display the enquiry format again. The bottom frame shows the reply from the system with details of contract and data of movements by

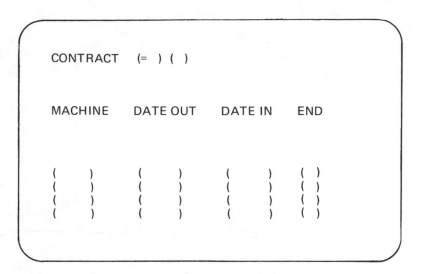

Fig. 13.7   Cursor in data entry

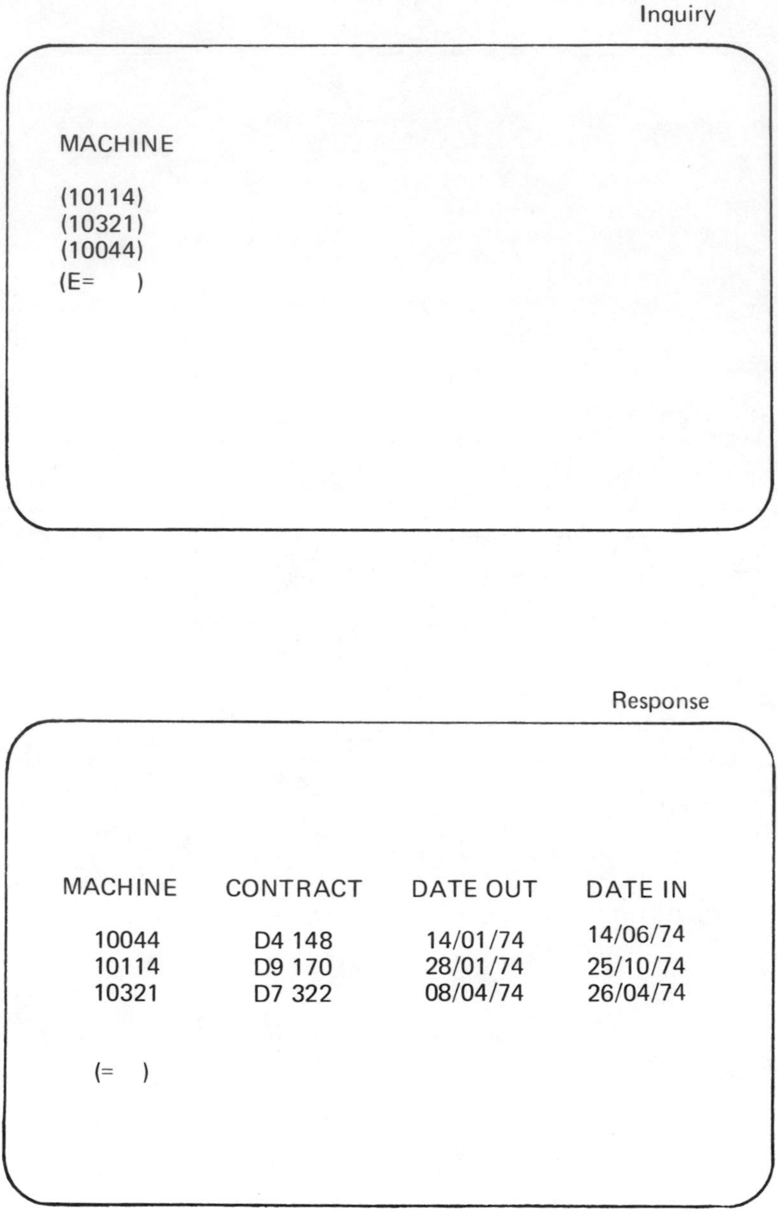

MACHINE

(10114)
(10321)
(10044)
(E=   )

MACHINE	CONTRACT	DATE OUT	DATE IN
10044	D4 148	14/01/74	14/06/74
10114	D9 170	28/01/74	25/10/74
10321	D7 322	08/04/74	26/04/74

(=   )

Fig. 13.8   Cursor in information retrieval

machine. The cursor is positioned to indicate that this is the end of the output.

Light Pen

The light pen is a photosensitive detector housed in a case that can be held in the hand. It is connected to the controls of the visual display unit by a cable. The operator points the end of the pen at a selected area of the screen. The field of view of the pen is about $\frac{1}{4}$ inch. When the operator depresses the associated function key, the pen senses the phosphor glow from the screen as the image is refreshed. Timing signals enable the computer system to interpret the signal received from the pen in terms of the position of the screen it was pointing at.

One application of this technique is selection of data for information retrieval. If, for example, the operator wanted details concerning a customer the spelling of whose name was uncertain, he could key in a request for a display of names and addresses of all customers with names "Warrick" and "Warwick." When these were displayed, he could point the pen at likely looking names for a further display of the details on record.

Another use of the pen is in interactive graphics systems, where it can be used to draw lines and symbols. There are a number of different methods associated with such systems. One requires that the operator touch two points on the screen and the system then generates a line connecting them. In another the light pen is pointed at a predetermined spot on the screen and then "draws" a line, the software generating an image on the screen as if the pen were pulling the spot out like an elastic band. Other systems use a "gravity field" concept to straighten lines and smooth curves. The pen need be used only within $\frac{1}{4}$ inch of where the line is intended. The screen is theoretically divided into a large number of points, each one with a gravity field around it. The nearest point will attract the line being drawn with the light pen. This is a very useful technique for stylized drawings such as engineering parts and statistical graphs. When the operator is satisfied with the image he has drawn, he depresses the transmit key and the image is sent to the central computer system for storage. Alternatively, it may be stored in local memory for transient use.

Rolling Ball

The rolling ball, or joystick, is an attachment that allows the operator to move the apparent field of view on the screen, draw a line or a curve, or store a position. The ball or stick can be moved along the x and y axes of the display to achieve the desired effect, depending on which function keys have been activated.

Effects that can be controlled with the rolling ball are windowing, zoom, rotation, and perspective. For *windowing,* the image on the screen is assumed to be a window looking onto the data or the graphical image displayed. The window can be moved to the left, right, up, or down to show a different view. As the window is moved to the right, for example, the part of the image at the left edge disappears and new information appears on the right, all intervening areas moving over accordingly. The illusion is produced by software that monitors the position of the rolling ball vis à vis the display and updates the display as necessary. *Zoom* moves the window in closer or pulls it away to decrease or increase the apparent distance of the viewer from the image, increasing or decreasing the amount of detail that can be seen accordingly. *Rotation* moves the orientation of the image around 360 degrees. *Perspective* does the same, except that the image is a three-dimensional one. Complex software is needed to control three-dimensional displays; one standard feature, for example, is the optional inhibition of hidden lines, which must, of course, be updated as the apparent perspective changes.

Rand Tablet

A Rand tablet is designed for the same functions as those provided by a light pen but the mechanics are different. The tablet is a conducting matrix fixed over the screen of the visual display unit. When the screen is touched with a stylus, input signals specifying the position are sent to the CPU. A light display is sent back to the screen as a visual double check for the operator.

Intensity Control

The relative brightness of the image projected onto the screen can have a strong effect on the ease of use of the visual display unit from the point of view of the operator. Overly bright lighting conditions in the room can wash out the image on the screen. If conditions are particularly bad, the glare can cause headaches and considerably reduced efficiency on the part of the operator. It may be necessary to install a viewing hood over the screen to eliminate this glare; most manufacturers offer these as accessories. Another optional feature with some terminals is an optical filter fixed over the screen to reduce surface reflection and increase contrast and brightness.

Most visual display units also have a knob, which can be used at the operator's option, to control the brightness of the display.

A further feature of software and hardware that can be very useful for data entry, information retrieval, and graphics applications is selected high brightness. Characters and lines can be highlighted in this way to draw attention to them and set them apart from other data on the screen. The cursor is usually set at maximum brightness, for example. Some models offer up to four different levels, but two or three are more practical and usually are sufficient for most applications. Unless there are special reasons to the contrary, it is usually best in a mixed alphanumeric-graphic display to highlight the characters, with the graphic portion a dimmer "background." Otherwise titles, headings, and legends tend to become lost.

Blinking

Blinking is a feature of hardware and software that is also useful for drawing attention to certain areas of the screen. Two different blink rates are a typical option. Single characters, fields, lines, or special symbols can be selected to blink. The technique can be used to call attention to errors in data entry, for example, or to highlight any factor that needs action on the part of the operator. One or two blinking items at a time on one screen are quite sufficient; if there are more than that, the operator can become distracted and even flustered.

Animation

Animation is a feature associated with graphics systems. If the software support is good, it can become a very powerful means of enhancing the usefulness of visual display; it provides a strong advantage over every other method of graphic computer output.

The concept of animation technique is fairly simple. Once the initial image has been sent from the CPU and displayed on the screen, selected portions are updated in sequence. When the frames change rapidly enough, the visual effect is one of animation. The traffic on the transmission lines need not be inordinately heavy, because only the changed portions of the display need be sent each time.

Uses of this feature are numerous in real-time applications. A counter can be updated, for example, to show increases or changes in prices, time, or physical processes, based either on actual data or on projections. Graphs and charts can be updated to show projections into the future. Models of various aspects of the organization's activities can be built and the effect of various contemplated changes shown as animated graphics. By photographing the screen an animated movie can be produced.

Reverse Field

To increase legibility and highlight certain images, it is possible with some terminals to display either dark images on a light background or light images on a dark background. One effective use of this technique is illustrated in Figure 13.9; other examples can be found in some of the other illustrations in this chapter.

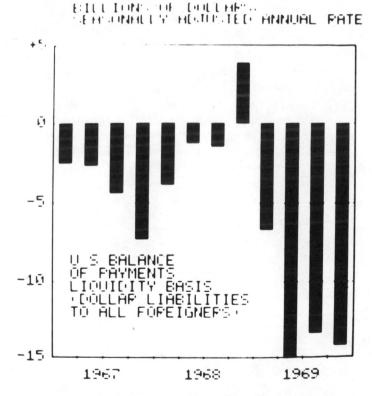

Fig. 13.9   Reverse field display (Courtesy Data Design Inc.)

Halftone and Color

Halftone and color displays are possible with some models of graphics terminals. The feature requires the use of more than one channel. An example of a color display is shown in Figure 13.10. Seven colors are used in the display. The background is black; titles, labels, and the graph axes are white; and from the top down the five graph lines are green, orange, red, blue, and purple. Three channels are needed to produce this display, as opposed to one for monotone displays.

The flexibility offered by the use of color, as well as the added interest and appeal of the display, should be obvious. Its use cannot be justified for all applications, however, particularly for those restricted to alphanumeric displays only. As with many of the other optional features available, the benefits need to be balanced against the extra hardware and software costs.

Hard-Copy Output

As was pointed out at the beginning of this chapter, one major advantage of teleprinters over visual display units is the hard copy of all input and output that is produced automatically. There are three methods of obtaining hard-copy output from visual display units. They are by fiber-optic reproduction, local teleprinter attached to the visual display unit, and printer connected to the CPU.

Fiber-Optic Reproduction. A visual display unit with a fiber-optic copier is shown in Figure 13.11. When the operator decides that he wants a copy of the display, he pushes the appropriate function key. The display is then "scanned" and the signals fed to a fiber-optic faceplate in the copier, which in turn deposits a latent image on paper. The image is then developed by a heat process. Quality of reproduction is good, and this method is one of choice for graphics systems. The copier in the illustration takes 20 minutes to warm up, but once this is done, a single copy is produced in 18 seconds (note also the joystick on the far left in the illustration).

Local Teleprinters. A locally attached teleprinter is the hard-copy facility offered by most alphanumeric visual display units. When the operator wants a copy of the display, he operates the print key and the frame is printed line by line on the teleprinter. The output speed is obviously that of the teleprinter. The visual display unit is automatically locked and cannot be used while printing is taking place. This method is suitable for low-volume, occasional hard copies, especially when it is necessary to conserve transmission time.

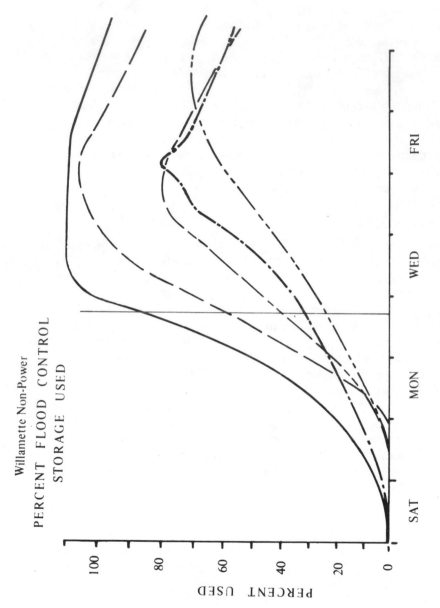

Willamette Non-Power
PERCENT FLOOD CONTROL
STORAGE USED

Fig. 13.10 Color display (Courtesy Data Disc, Inc.)

174

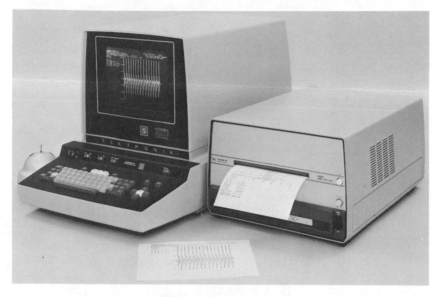

Fig. 13.11 Fiber-optic copier (Courtesy Teletronix, Inc.)

Attached Printer. The third method allows the operator to specify from the visual display unit that the current display is to be printed. The data is then printed from the central CPU on a print device located either locally or at the main computer center. The visual display unit can continue to be used while printing is going on. This is more suitable for higher-volume output. For very high-volume printing, a further option would be to store the print image on high-speed media at the computer center for printing and delivery to the user later.

A further extension of the method described above can be used when the full text of the information required by the user is not stored on computer files. This situation often exists in information retrieval systems designed around technical papers or very high-volume hardcopy material, such as newspaper clippings. An abstract of the material is stored on computer files and indexed. The user at the terminal can "browse" and select abstracts for display through the use of key words and codes. When he finds an item that looks as if it is of particular interest, he can send a message to the central computer system. The message is passed on, either immediately to another terminal or in batch mode, perhaps overnight. A full copy of the information is then made and sent to the user. This might be a photocopy or a microfiche.

OPERATOR INSTRUCTIONS

From the descriptions given above of the various display options available to the systems designer it is obvious that very complex systems can be built around visual display units. Furthermore the terminals may be scattered around a number of different remote locations and used by a large number of people. User training and system implementation therefore loom large as major tasks for the systems team.

The success of any real-time system is largely dependent on the people who will operate it and, one hopes, benefit from it. It is essential to train thoroughly at all levels. A basic beginning must be a course on introduction to computers for those without previous experience with computer systems. The course chosen should concentrate on real-time, as opposed to batch, systems. The importance of accurate input and procedural discipline should be stressed. From there the next step would be detailed training about what the new system will do and how it is to be used. Any resentment or resistance to the new system at this stage of the project is usually due to insufficient training and lack of general awareness; if any signs of such restiveness appear, corrective action must be taken immediately. The success of the system when it is implemented depends on the attitudes of the users.

Specific training of the terminal operators presents other problems. The hardware may not be available for training until very near the date for systems testing. This problem can be overcome by developing a simple keyboard training system that begins as soon as the first terminals are installed, even before they are connected to the network. The operators can then become familiar with the equipment and with at least some of the problems of on-line working. The training schedule can be stepped up as the full system becomes available.

During systems testing, and for new staff joining after the system is implemented, some method must be found for initial training that does not put the system in jeopardy from errors. This may be done by operating the system on dummy files outside of normal working hours or by building into the system at the design stage a "training mode" of operation. This latter method is very satisfactory in that the trainee sees the system operating normally on live data, with the exception that file updating is invisibly locked out.

It is the responsibility of management and of the systems team to develop early into the project contingency plans for those situations that almost inevitably arise and cannot be prevented. The principal ones are staff who find that they just cannot adapt to the new system; staff who are trained satisfactorily but then leave for one reason or another; and the necessity for temporary staff who will be needed to run the manual system during the training period for terminal operators and up to full-scale implementation of the new system.

PART FOUR

GRAPHIC OUTPUT

CHAPTER 14

Graphic Output from the Line Printer

The limitations of the high-speed line printer are very severe; much more so, in fact, than is usually recognized by systems analysts and programmers who have never had other types of hard-copy output devices available. The limitations are in part due to the mechanical construction of the device and the associated software commands that can be given to it, and in part due to its relatively slow speed, which demands that output be designed to print as quickly as possible. This leads, for example, to forms that are very wide in proportion to their depth and also in proportion to standard sizes of paper in use elsewhere in the company, so that as much data as possible can be printed on one line. This and other restrictions imposed by line printers were discussed in some detail in Part Two.

A report produced in any other part of the company always means a *written* report, that is, narrative organized into sentences and paragraphs and then typed. If the sales department issues a document called "Report on New Product Marketing Strategy," or the personnel department produces one on "Recommendations for Flexible Working Hours," or even when the data processing department develops a "Five-Year Plan for Data Base Development," we would expect to see a narrative report *supported by* tables and diagrams. When a computer system produces a "report," however, it consists of tabular material only. This is not to suggest that computer reports should be narrative in character, only to point out the differences in the meaning of "report" when it is the output of a computer system. Most such output is in tabular form—data arranged in rows and columns—of the type that is considered to be supporting information in other contexts. A computer that can compose grammatical English prose has yet to be built.

When a computer-produced report is seen in this light, as a supporting document, it then follows that the user of the report must bring to it other knowledge in order to make full use of the information. It is not enough to see that sales of Product *A* are up and those of Product *B* are down. Is this a seasonal variation? How does it correlate with advertising expenditure and salesman's commissions? What has the competition been doing? Will they react to this change, and if so, how? What does it mean in relation to the state of the economy and changing consumer buying patterns? There is, however, an even more important judgment that the user must make, which is whether the changing sales pattern is something he should take action on or whether it is within normal limits and no case for worry.

ADVANTAGES OF GRAPHIC OUTPUT

The example above serves to illustrate the two kinds of information user management needs from reports of this type: They are interested in the *relationships between different variables* (sales versus time of year, increase in advertising expenditures versus increase in sales) and in *exceptional situations* (unexpected increase or decrease, change in usual averages or proportions). The possibilities of reporting on only these exceptions were discussed in Part Two; this chapter is going a step further to consider a different way of presenting the information.

The two categories of information—relationships between variables, and exceptions—are often more meaningful if shown in graphic rather than tabular form. In a report produced by hand instead of by computer they probably would be illustrated that way. There are several important reasons for this, as follows.

1. Graphic illustrations are easier to understand, especially when the user is looking for comparisons or exceptions. Many computer-produced tabulations are, in fact, used as raw data for drawing graphs because the key aspects are far easier to understand in that format.
2. They are more compact. Many pages of printer listing can be reduced to one diagram. This is even more true when the really interesting facts are the exceptions.

3. The data can be seen in two dimensions, as opposed to a "one-dimensional" list of figures. This is particularly useful for showing relationships between variables.
4. There is more flexibility in ways of showing emphasis, drawing attention to key areas, and making the data easier to understand.
5. Charts and graphs are more useful for study by a group of people, either in a meeting or informally. Pointing out features of a diagram is easier than searching through pages of a listing.

WAYS OF PRODUCING GRAPHIC OUTPUT

There are several methods of producing graphic output from the computer, classified by the type of equipment used. Perhaps the most obvious is by graph plotter; this method is discussed in detail in the next chapter. Two others are by use of microfilm, as was shown in Chapter 9, or displayed by a visual display unit, which was covered in Part Three.

If it is possible to produce pictures of John F. Kennedy, Peanuts' characters, or naked ladies on a line printer (most readers will have seen such examples), it is certainly possible to produce useful charts and diagrams for business purposes, probably with less effort and ingenuity.

When a decision is made to try to use the line printer this way, there are then two possible paths: a specified and hand-coded program or a software package. Many good packages are available for this purpose; they are discussed in Chapter 19, and some examples will be found in Appendix B. But whether the designer's job is to prepare specifications for a programmer or create the parameters for a software package, most of the design considerations are the same. The rest of this chapter is devoted to the principles of designing graphics for the line printer, with examples.

Design Method

The following steps are recommended as a guide to design methodology for graphic output from the line printer.

Collection of All Relevant Information.   If this has not already been done in an earlier stage of the project, it is now necessary to determine how the data will be used and the ranges of the values it can have. This should be done by interviewing the users concerned and by referring to input forms, existing reports, and other relevant documentation. This step is essential for ultimately producing useful graphics; how the information is used will be shown below.

Collection of Samples of Live Data.   This can be done in concert with the first step. The samples should be a representative range, including "typical" cases as well as those at the extremes of minimum and maximum values. These will be used in trial designs and for producing mock-ups for approval.

Choice of a Suitable Type of Chart.   There are only a few basic types that give good results when done within the limitations of the spacing and character set of a computer line printer. They are described below.

Preliminary Sketches.   Preliminary sketches can be fairly rough, being done to try out scales and positioning of the data to be included.

Preliminary Printer Layout.   Working from the rough sketch the chart can be positioned by laying it out on the form supplied by the manufacturer for this purpose. Alterations may have to be made to fit the chart within the dimensions of the paper it will be printed on. At this stage the extreme ranges of the data should be tried out to ensure that any set of values can be accommodated within the size and proportions chosen. Reprogramming after the system is installed can be very expensive.

Consultation with the User.   Users knowledgeable about computer procedure may be able to offer comments on a printer layout, but actual mocked-up samples are much better. They can either be done in full scale on a typewriter or a utility program can be used to produce "dummies" on the line printer.

Consultation with the Programming Section.   Most programmers will find the design and coding problem for line-printer graphics interesting and enjoyable work. An experienced programmer will probably be able to offer suggestions for minor alterations to the layout that will simplify the job considerably. If a software package is to be used, a double-check now will assure that the design can be handled by the package.

Preparation of Final Specifications.   When the layout has been approved by the user, with his suggestions for alterations incorporated, the chart should be documented with printer layout specifications and any necessary notes for the programmer, following installation standards.

TYPES OF GRAPHICS

The most useful types of graphic output for the line printer are bar charts, histograms, graphs, and scattergrams. Each is described in turn.

Bar Charts

A bar chart shows comparisons of a small number of variables expressed with the length of the bar in proportion to the size of the number it represents. An example with horizontal bars is shown in Figure 14.1.

An illustration of a vertical bar chart is shown in Figure 14.2. Vertical bars usually require more complex programming logic, but sometimes, as in the case with the data in Figure 14.2, the chart is much easier to read if the bars are vertical. (Figure 14.2 also illustrates the advantage of graphic presentation over a table; it is much easier to pick out the exceptions—that is, best and worst salesman—from the graph than from the table. Note that the cutoff point of the vertical scale "loses" salesmen with less than $15,000 sales.)

Histograms

A histogram looks something like a bar chart, but there are two important differences. A bar chart is used when the data does not represent a continuous variable, a histogram when it does. Bars on a bar chart do not touch; those on a histogram do. An easy way to decide which is which is to think of the tops of the bars forming a graph; this would obviously be nonsense for the data shown in Figures 14.1 and 14.2 but would be more meaningful for the example in Figure 14.3. A histogram should be chosen instead of a graph, however, when there are not enough points available to plot a smooth curved line; smoothing the tops of the bars in Figure 14.3 would not only be less useful, it would actually be misleading.

A variation of the histogram, called a "profile chart," is shown in Figure 14.4. This is identical with Figure 14.3 except that the continuation lines of the bars have been omitted. Figure 14.4 also serves to illustrate how the histogram could be turned into a graph if more data points were available for smoothing.

Graphs

A graph shows the relationship between variables as a smoothed line plotted against two axes. Because it is not possible to draw a

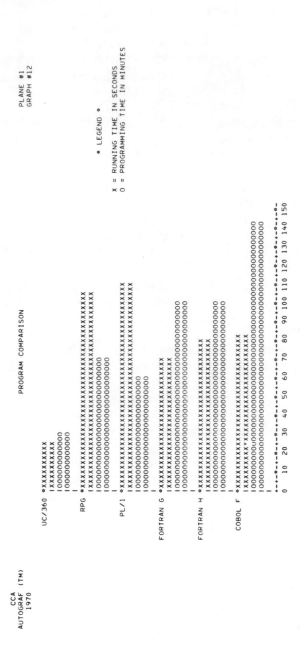

Fig. 14.1 Horizontal bar chart (Produced by AUTOGRAF. Courtesy Cambridge Computer Associates, Inc.)

186

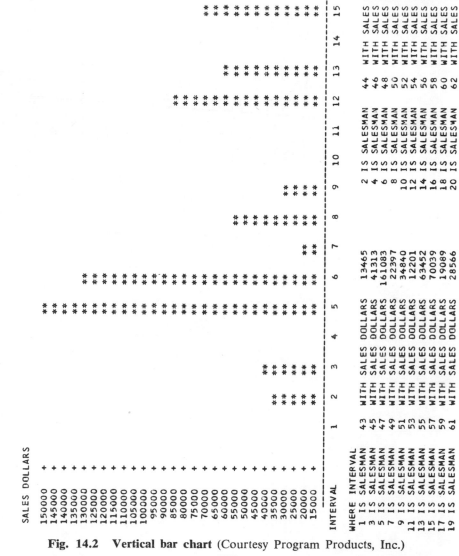

Fig. 14.2 **Vertical bar chart** (Courtesy Program Products, Inc.)

187

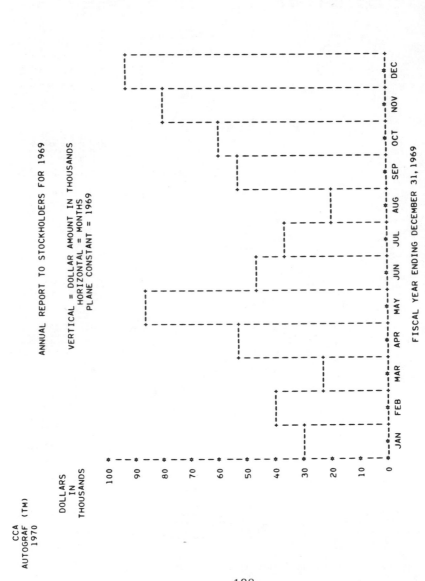

Fig. 14.3 Histogram (Produced by AUTOGRAF. Courtesy Cambridge Computer Associates, Inc.)

188

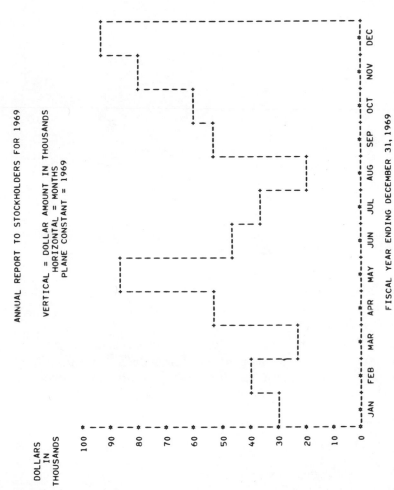

Fig. 14.4 Profile chart (Produced by AUTOGRAF. Courtesy Cambridge Computer Associates, Inc.)

189

line, straight or curved, with the line printer, the best that can be produced is an approximation to a line. There is an example in Figure 14.5 showing the use of the printer's special characters to indicate a

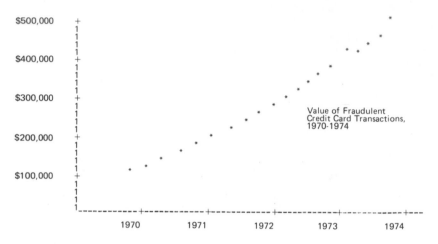

Fig. 14.5   Example of graph produced on line printer

curved line. This type of graph would be useful for showing trends but not suitable for reading exact values.

Scatter Diagrams

A scatter diagram, or scattergram, is useful for plotting a number of points when smoothing them into a line for a graph would be misleading. A scatter diagram will show clusters, groupings, and exceptions without distorting the data. An example is shown in Figure 14.6. Scattergrams are particularly easy to produce on the line printer because they require points rather than lines or bars.

DESIGN CRITERIA

Standard charting conventions are summarized in Figure 14.7. Following these conventions not only simplifies the designer's task, it also ensures that the user of the chart finds it easy to interpret.

In addition, there are some rules of thumb that are recommended

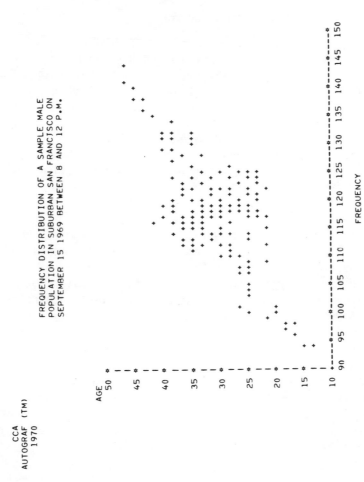

Fig. 14.6 **Scattergram** (Produced by AUTOGRAF. Courtesy Cambridge Computer Associates, Inc.)

191

Always include a clear, explanatory title, with additional notes or subtitles
   if necessary.
Put the independent variable on the horizontal (x) axis and the dependent
   variable on the vertical (y) axis. The dependent variable is the one
   that is changing; for example, income in dollars is the dependent variable plotted against time; miles per gallon of gasoline is the dependent
   variable plotted against average speed in miles per hour.
State the units of measurement along each axis.
Label each axis clearly.
Leave wide margins on all sides.
Indicate scale on axis, but do not overcrowd scale markers.

Fig. 14.7   Conventions for charts and graphs

for designing line-printer graphics. Because it is not possible to draw
straight lines with the printer, the output can look messy and be difficult
to read unless care is taken. First, plain unlined continuous forms are
preferable to lined stock paper, and only one chart should be printed
per page. If the output volume is low, using high-quality paper will
considerably improve the appearance of the finished product. If the
output volume is high, it might be worth investing in preprinted forms
with the axes already drawn, eliminating one of the drawbacks of the
printer; this would require special care on the part of the operators to
align the forms properly, as is the case with checks and other preprinted forms.

   Careful thought should be given to the special characters chosen to
indicate lines and bars. If in doubt, it should not be difficult to run
some samples to see the result. The examples in Figure 14.1 through
14.6 will provide suggestions; note the use of the hyphen, asterisk, plus
sign, and so on. Because the use of color is not possible, characters of
markedly different shapes must be chosen to show contrast, for example,
the X and O bars in Figure 14.1. Also, the results of mixing more
than three such groups of characters on the same chart will be too
cluttered to understand easily.

   Not more than three sets of data should be shown on the same
chart unless they are so closely related logically that proper understanding is not possible otherwise. Special care is necessary in choosing
symbols if lines cross; it may be necessary to have an unrealistic gap
because of the limitations of the printer.

SUMMARY

Graphical presentation of data can often be more useful than tabular listings. Computer-produced graphical output is possible even when the only tool available to the designer is the line printer, and charts or graphs should be considered for any material that lends itself to this type of layout. Because of the limitations of the line printer, however, care must be taken to keep the charts as simple as possible for clarity and ease of use.

CHAPTER 15

Graph Plotting

A graph plotter is a computer-controlled device that moves a writing instrument over a surface, usually a sheet of paper, to produce a graphic image. Graph plotters are often called "digital plotters" because they are controlled by the digital signals from the computer. There are a number of different methods of classifying plotters, but the most frequently used one is by the way the plotting surface is mounted, that is, drum versus flatbed. A drum plotter writes on continuous stationery that moves lengthwise under the plotting head in one direction while the writing instrument moves back and forth in the other direction. A flatbed plotter has a plotting head that moves along both axes while the sheet of paper remains stationary. More detail about plotting technology will be given below.

The use of graph plotters for commercial and management applications had been slow to develop, although its versatility in other fields cannot be denied. Competing methods include computer-output microfilm, real-time displays on a visual display terminal, and electrostatic printer-plotters. (The first two of these have been discussed in earlier sections of this book. Printer-plotters are covered in the next chapter.) Even so, systems analysts should be aware of graph plotter techniques and applications. One reason for this is that as ease of implementation increases and as the cost decreases, graph plotters become more competitive with other methods. The other is that many organizations have or will soon have plotters installed for scientific or engineering applications. With the plotter already on hand and paid for, as it were, the cost justification for using it for management information becomes much more feasible.

194

In this chapter the diversity of the application areas for graph plotters will be outlined, followed by a description of plotter technology. Finally, software and systems considerations will be discussed. The emphasis throughout will be on the commercial uses of graph plotters and the information they can supply to management; a number of illustrations of such plotter output will be given.

APPLICATIONS

The first plotters, developed in the 1940s, were analog devices. Because of the greater flexibility and higher accuracy of digital devices, especially digital computers, the development of analog technology became restricted to a few specialized areas. Any analog device attached to a digital controller, or vice versa, requires a control unit to convert the signals. As digital computers came to dominate the data processing field, so did plotter technology become more oriented toward digital instead of analog devices.

The major impetus for improvements in digital plotters has been historically from the field of automatic drafting. Many of the plotters at the upper end of the range, both in terms of power and of cost, have been developed especially for this use. An automatic drafting system has at its heart, almost by definition, a flatbed plotter. More will be said about such a system later.

Scientific applications have provided another major influence for advances in plotting technology. These include cartography, special-purpose maps such as geological maps, census and survey maps, and weather maps; monitoring and diagrammatic representation of biological and medical processes; wind tunnel patterns (one of the earliest applications); and research in electronics.

Engineering applications are equally important. Digital plotters are rivaled only by interactive graphics via a visual display unit as the engineering designer's most important automated tool. Specific application areas here include printed circuit artwork, architecture, numerical control patterns, logic diagrams, aircraft lofting and layout, design of tools for automobile production, structural geometry, drawings of components, petrochemical processing charts, shipbuilding, and even row boats. Another application area that should be mentioned is pattern design and cloth cutting for the tailoring business.

The entry of graph plotter techniques into the management area has been through flowcharts, critical path networks, stock performance charts, and statistical and financial analysis. The advantages of presenting data for management graphically were stressed in the last chapter; the reasons for the slow advances of graph plotting in this area were mentioned above. Nevertheless, use of plotters for this application area continues to increase, and the indications are that plotter manufacturers are turning their attention more and more to developing this potential market, especially through software aimed at business applications.

PLOTTING TECHNOLOGY

Various ways of classifying plotters include the type of plotting surface, the recording technique and mode of operation, the method of specifying the plot, the size of the plotter, the accuracy of the output, and the cost; but as was pointed out earlier, the most popular classification is by the mounting of the plotting surface, that is, drum versus flatbed plotters (there are a few specialized devices that fit into neither category).

Flatbed Plotters

In a flatbed plotter the output medium (usually paper) is fixed to a horizontal table. The plot is created by the movement of a carriage and the writing-tool assembly fixed to it. An example of a flatbed plotter can be seen in Figure 15.1. The carriage moves along one axis while the writing assembly moves on the carriage along the other axis.

The output medium is held in place by a vacuum from below. In addition to paper this can be photographic film, mylar, vellum, plate glass, art board, sheet metal, or almost any other substance that will accept an image, provided the correct drawing tool is used. The drawing tools can be pencil, liquid ink pen, ball-point pen, felt-tip pen, an incising or cutting tool, a thermochromic tool, a photoplotting head, or some other specialized device. Multipen holders for different colors and line thicknesses are available.

The size of the plotting area is variable depending on the device and the options chosen at purchase time. The smallest is about 11 by 17 inches; bigger systems go up to 8 feet in width and 12 or 14 feet in length. Some plotters will step the paper across the plotting table for plots of up to 24 feet in length.

The speed of the plot also varies widely, depending on the device.

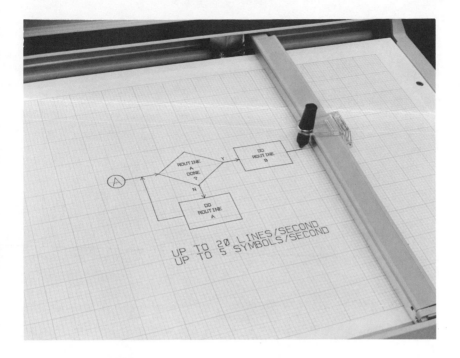

Fig. 15.1 Flatbed plotter (Courtesy Hewlett-Packard)

At the top of the range, speeds of up to 40 inches per second can be attained, but a typical range is 1 to 12 inches per second. The accuracy of the recording is very high for flatbed plotters, being in the range of ± 0.05 inches to ± 0.005 inches.

Automatic Drafting Systems

A large segment of the market for flatbed plotters is automatic drafting systems. Such a system consists of a digital flatbed plotter, an image digitizer, and appropriate attachments and control units. The image digitizer is used for input, the plotter for output. A manually controlled cursor can be moved over the plotting surface by the draftsman; the cursor, through the image digitizer, generates digital signals that are stored on magnetic tape, giving a representation of what has been drawn. A library of graphical data can thus be built up, modified, and redrawn as needed. Automatic drafting is used for engineering drawings, architectural plans, elevation diagrams, and similar applications.

Drum Plotters

Drum-type plotters have a movable writing medium moving under a fixed writing arm. An illustration will be found in Figure 15.2. The

Fig. 15.2   Drum plotter (Courtesy CalComp)

arm has attached to it a writing tool that can move back and forth across the width of the paper. Thus if the paper is held stationary while the writing head moves, a line is drawn across the paper; if the writing head remains in one position while the paper moves, a line is drawn down the length of the paper. Obviously by moving both at once, skewed lines can be drawn. The angle of such a line to the horizontal or vertical axis depends on the relative speed of the paper and the writing head. Most drum plotters can draw lines in eight directions, that is, two backwards and forwards, two crosswise, and one each in two directions at a 45 degree angle to the x and y axes. This is illustrated in Figure 15.3. A few devices can draw in 16 or 24 directions.

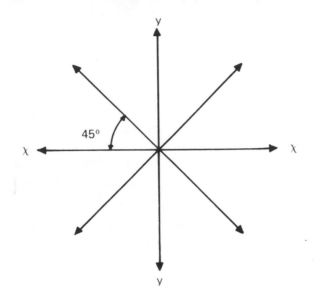

Fig. 15.3   Eight-vector drum plotter movement

Under program control, the writing pen can be raised or lowered for "line" or "no line."

Because the writing head and paper movements permit only straight lines to be drawn, curves are represented by increments of lines (it should be noted that some flatbed plotters also operate this way). The result is a jagged or stepped appearance, its severity depending on the size of the line increments. Step sizes vary from 0.01 inches to 0.00125 inches. Typical plotting speeds are in the range of 2 to 26 inches per second.

Drum plotter writing media are limited to materials that can be rolled or fan folded for feeding across the drum; this means paper, with an ink pen writing device. Continuous stationery for drum plotters is available in widths of 12 to 36 inches. Plain, unlined paper is most often used, but the drum plotter forms are available as graph paper of various linear scales in metric or Imperial (inches) format, and as semi-log or log-log graphs.

Drum versus Flatbed

Generally speaking, drum-type plotters are cheaper and faster than the flatbed type but not as versatile or as accurate. Drum plotters range from compact, virtually desk-top models to large devices that rival flatbeds for accuracy. They are restricted in the output medium, although using rolls of paper means that the machine can be left running unattended for relatively long periods. Drum plotters are easier to set up and use, but accurate registration on preprinted forms can be difficult. Flatbed plotters offer a wider range of options, including a variety of types of writing heads and writing media. The very high degree of accuracy possible with flatbed types, coupled with writing head and writing media flexibility, means that they are more suited for specialized applications such as automatic drafting, which was described briefly above.

All of these considerations mean that for most business applications, drum-type plotters are the device of choice over flatbed types. Business charts and graphs require neither the high degree of accuracy necessary for scientific and engineering applications nor the versatility of writing heads offered by flatbed plotters. The unsophisticated control mechanism, with its ease of installation, ease of use, and low cost, is more likely to fit into a management information data processing budget. The exception would be when a flatbed plotter is already in use for other applications within the organization, its slack time being easily adapted to business graphics.

SYSTEMS CONSIDERATIONS

Programming and Software

One of the reasons for the relative lack of success of digital plotters in the business information market has been, as with other hardware devices, a notable lack of software to support them. Programming is complicated and expensive and usually must be done in FORTRAN or some other scientific or low-level language. A separate control command is needed for every step or increment to be made by the writing head and another for every increment of the paper. This is a very complex and specialized programming task, even for the simplest of graphs. The absence of prewritten standard routines makes it too expensive for most commercial installations.

Software routines are needed for all standard operations. These include drawing axes and standard curves; drawing characters for labeling; the generation of three-dimensional and perspective views; contouring; and the generation of standard shapes such as triangles and squares.

The software that is available falls roughly into three categories: standard subroutines for functions such as those described above; application-oriented packages for areas such as numerical control, engineering, and flowcharting; and programs for processing and preparing raw data for the plot—for example, generating a critical path network from data on resources and timescales. Some in-house programming is still required, whether it is merely specifying input parameters for an applications package or writing routines in a high-level language like COBOL to link together the FORTRAN subroutines supplied by the plotter manufacturer.

Some examples of plots produced from packaged software are shown here. Figure 15.4 was produced on a Hewlett-Packard device with a small number of special command statements linked to pre-written subroutines for drawing the axes, setting the scale of the plot, drawing the graph lines, and drawing the symbols. Figures 15.5 and 15.6 show two different ways of representing the same data graphically. Both were produced by CalComp's Datagraph Automatic Graph Generator, a package espeically developed for business-oriented graphs and charts. More details about this and other plotter software will be found in Appendix B.

Generation of three-dimensional and perspective views is an even more specialized programming problem. One widely used software package for this purpose is CalComp's THREE-D. It will produce three-dimensional drawings from any data that can be expressed as a single valued function of two variables, or as XYZ coordinates. Options include deleting hidden lines and varying the size and apparent distortion of the drawing. Stereo pairs can be produced for viewing with a stereoscopic viewer not very different from the stereo viewers of our grandfathers' long winter nights; or the software can be used to control a computer output microfilm for producing animated movies. An example of business-oriented plot drawn by THREE-D is shown in Figure 15.7.

On-Line versus Off-Line

Another of the reasons for the slow acceptance of graph plotters in commercial installations has been their very slow speed in relation to the

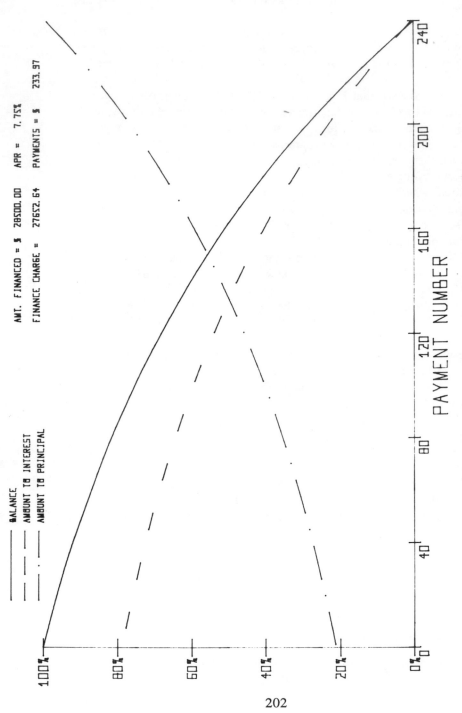

Fig. 15.4 **Three-line graph plot** (Courtesy Hewlett-Packard)

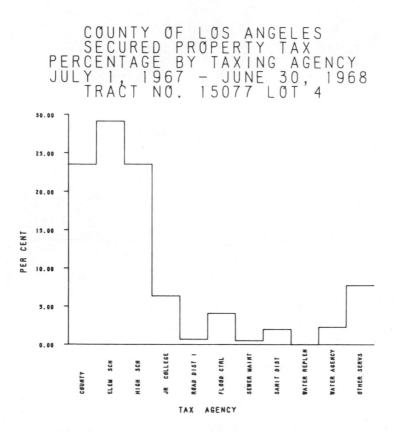

Fig. 15.5 Histogram plot (Courtesy CalComp)

speed of the central computer. In the days of first- and second-generation computers, the data transfer rate of a fast graph plotter was twice
that of the central processor. Today the computer is 1000 times faster.
A plotter on-line to the computer, even with most of the control functions transferred from the computer to a plotter graphics controller, is
an uneconomic proposition for all but the most specialized applications.

Running the plotter off-line, however, changes the situation considerably. There are two possibilities. For a very large flatbed plotter,
a dedicated minicomputer, either linked to the plotter via control
units or built in, is the answer for some scientific and engineering applications. Otherwise the best solution is usually to supply the data to be
plotted on a magnetic tape created on the main-frame computer, with

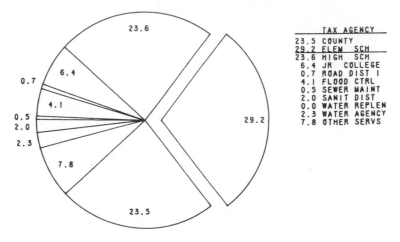

Fig. 15.6 Pie chart plot (Courtesy CalComp)

standard graphics routines fed in from a cassette tape loaded into the plotter controller. This method gives compatibility and flexibility, taking advantage of the speed of the host computer without degrading its operation with the slow plotter.

SUMMARY

This chapter has given an overview of the application areas and technology of digital graph plotters. Their acceptance in the business world as a graphics tool has been, and probably will remain, limited by a number of factors. These are slow plotting speeds in comparison to main-frame computing speeds; complicated programming requirements and lack of business-oriented software; and the versatility, speed, and low cost of alternative methods of graphic production. Nevertheless the wide acceptance of plotting in other areas, notably automatic drafting, engineering, and scientific applications, means that the impetus for tech-

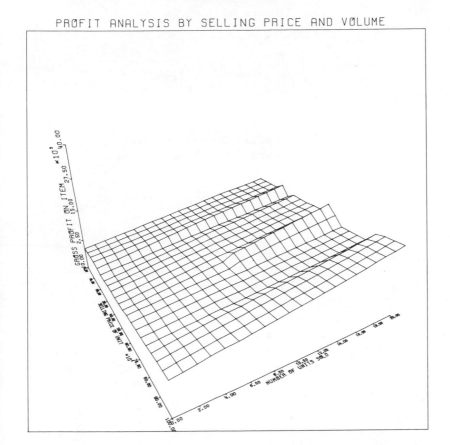

PROFIT ANALYSIS BY SELLING PRICE AND VOLUME

Fig. 15.7 Three-dimensional plot (Courtesy CalComp)

nological and software improvements does exist and is, in fact, being utilized by some plotter manufacturers. Plotting cannot therefore be ruled out as one possible method of giving management business statistics in graphic form.

CHAPTER 16

Printer-Plotters

A relatively new entrant into the graphics field is the electrostatic nonimpact line printer. The way in which the printing mechanism works makes it possible for the device to produce lines and curves as well as shaped characters. Some electrostatic printer-plotters can operate in print mode and plot mode alternately to produce alphanumeric data and graphics on the same page, whereas others can operate in both modes simultaneously for the added flexibility of graphic and alphanumeric output on the same line. Electrostatic technology and application areas were described in some detail in the chapter on printers (Chapter 4) but there the emphasis was on alphanumeric output. This chapter concentrates on the plotting capability of the devices, but some of the details given in Chapter 4 must necessarily be repeated here.

We begin with a description of the electrostatic writing technique, especially as it is utilized for graphics. There is then a discussion of the advantages, disadvantages, and suitability of electrostatic printing for various applications. Plotting software for these devices will be mentioned, too.

PRINCIPLES OF OPERATION

In an electrostatic printer the only moving parts are the paper transport. The writing head is a stationary linear array of conducting nibs. Nonconducting dielectric paper is used. Signals are sent to the conducting nibs from the computer or other digital control unit. A charge is placed on the paper by each nib that has been activated. The image is then developed by passing the paper through liquid toner. The paper is moved by a friction drive system. As it emerges from the toner, an air blower system dries it; no other developing or fixing is required.

An illustration of the operating principle of an electrostatic printer was shown in Figure 4.5. Figure 4.6 was a photograph of the writing head. Typically, there are 100 writing nibs per inch in the writing head. Characters and lines are formed on the matrix principle; example character lines were shown in Figure 4.7. Graphic output production is shown in Figure 16.1. The nibs are set about 0.01 inches apart; plotting density is thus up to 10,000 points per square inch. The dot matrix for an alphabetic or numeric character is usually either 5 x 7, 7 x 9, or 16 x 16. Printing is done at a rate of 1.2 to 1.6 inches per second, or up to 1000 alphanumeric lines per second, depending on the device. The method of imprinting or scanning means that errors are not cumulative. Any skew or misalignment on one scan is not carried over to the next, as could happen with a conventional plotter.

The paper used may be in fanfold or roll form. It can be written on in the ordinary way with pencil or pen, keeps well in long-term storage, is not sensitive to light, and can be reproduced on office copying machines. Preprinted forms can be supplied. Paper movement is accomplished by friction, the assembly being a stepper motor. For fanfolded paper, a black mark is placed by the fold on the back of each sheet for sensing by an optical device in the printer. There are thus no sprocket holes, and accuracy of registration on the page is relatively high.

The maximum width of a plot can vary from 7.75 inches to 18 inches, depending on the device. Character print lines vary from 80 characters to 140 characters, with 132 being typical. Printing can be done in upper and lower case and in a variety of type fonts, including special characters sets for foreign languages.

SOFTWARE

Electrostatic printer-plotter manufacturers supply basic plotting routines with their machines. The software and, of course, interfacing control units, are available for a wide range of computers, with the emphasis on the small computer range. Standard software routines include vector generation, drawing of axes, scales, and labels, scaling data to the plot, generation of alphanumeric characters of various sizes, grid production, and shading. User-written routines usually call for FORTRAN or assembly language coding.

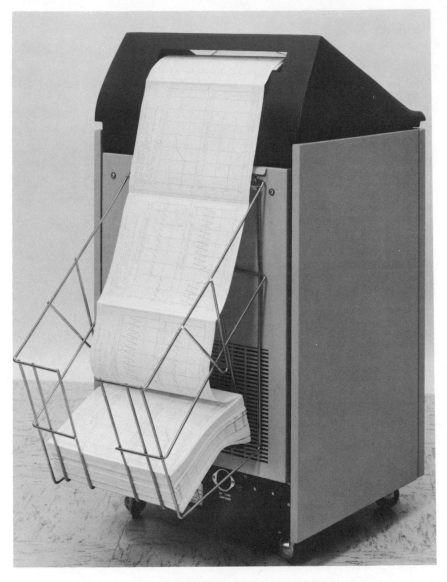

Fig. 16.1 Electrostatic printer-plotter (Courtesy Versatec)

OFF-LINE PLOTTING

The major manufacturers of electrostatic printer-plotters offer off-line options as well. The data is formatted and written out to a magnetic tape on the main-frame computer. The tape is then loaded into an off-line tape reader to drive the plotter. Some options that are available are a "file select" feature for search and selection of data on the tape, and repetitive printing of the same file for multiple copies.

ADVANTAGES AND DISADVANTAGES

As was pointed out in Chapter 4 major advantages of electrostatic devices are their lack of moving parts, reliability, low down time, and low maintenance cost. They are, in fact, remarkably trouble-free. They are also inexpensive, purchase or rental price being one-third to one-fifth that of the average impact printer.

On the other hand the fact that only one copy at a time can be made is a major drawback for many installations. Producing multiple copies, or photocopying the original, is both time consuming and expensive. There is also the need for special paper and for maintaining a supply of the liquid toner and refilling the machine with it. The slow speed, relative to the fastest of the impact printers for alphanumeric work, is an inhibiting factor for some potential users, too.

Electrostatic printer-plotters have found most favor in installations with small-to-medium computers requiring an inexpensive graphics capability. They are also popular as remote hard-copy output devices linked to cathode-ray tube terminals in on-line networks; their silent operation makes them particularly suitable for office, as opposed to machine room, environments. Custom-built or modified machines are also available from the manufacturers for use in a "hostile" environment or streamlined for higher speed for certain applications. Tailored software can be supplied, too.

These printer-plotters seem to have a permanent and growing niche in the business data processing world. They give all the advantages of graphics within quite acceptable limits of cost and accuracy, especially compared to digital plotters. Their use will spread as a wider choice of packaged software for producing graphics becomes available.

PART FIVE

SPECIAL DESIGN CONSIDER- ATIONS

CHAPTER 17

Turnaround Documents

A turnaround card or document is one that is produced as output from the computer system, receives various kinds of manual handling and processing, and eventually comes back into the system in the input stream. Additional data may or may not have been added in the meantime. The justification for turnaround input is to avoid unnecessary keying and input preparation when some or all of the data needed already exist within the system's master files. Turnaround transactions are distinguished from files that are output from the system, held, and then read back in the next run (for example, for updating) by virtue of the fact that manual, that is, human, use is made of the turnaround before it reaches the system again as input.

Most turnaround items are either punched cards or documents for direct reading: optical character recognition (OCR) or optical mark reading (OMR). Optical character recognition and optical mark reading are usually classified as input rather than output methods; therefore details of reading and handling equipment and design considerations will not be given here. The interested reader is referred to Wooldridge (1973a) in the Bibliography for a more exhaustive text.

EXAMPLE APPLICATIONS

Some examples of applications using turnaround documents follow. *Updating the Product Master File after an Inventory.* Figures 17.1 and 17.2 illustrate in a simplified form updating after an inventory. Just before a full inventory is to be taken—in this example it is

213

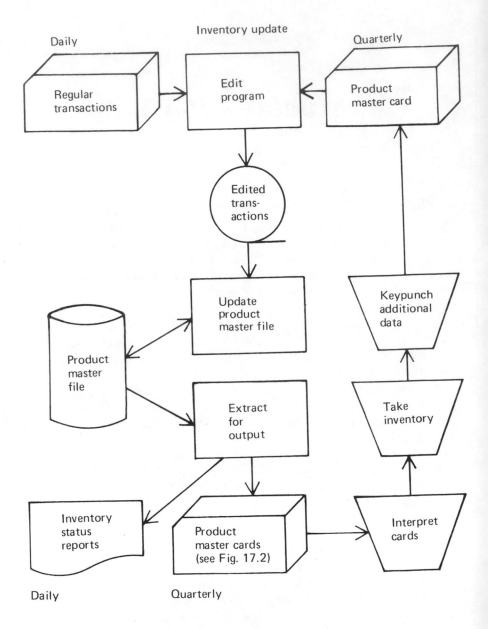

Fig. 17.1 Example of turnaround card system

214

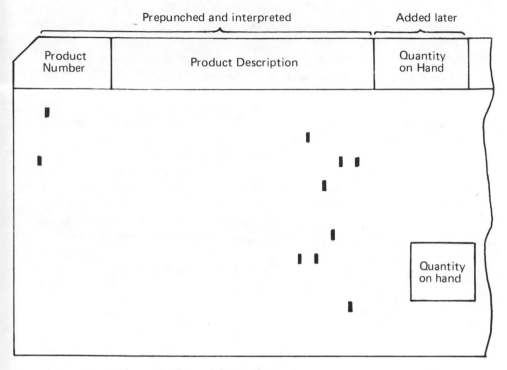

Fig. 17.2   Example of turnaround card

quarterly—the computer system (triggered either by date or control card) produces a punched card for each product in stock. The card contains the prepunched product number and description. The cards are interpreted and then distributed to the staff doing the inventory. As each item is counted, the quantity on hand is written on the card. The cards then go back to the data preparation department where the quantity is punched. The cards then become input to the next computer run to update the product master file. Before any quantity-on-hand fields are corrected on the master file, it is useful to print a report showing discrepancies between book stock and actual stock. A variation of this plan would be to prepunch also the quantity on hand, which could be taken from the master file. Human action would then be necessary only if the actual count differed. The danger here is that human beings tend to take the easy way out, and may assume the card is correct without doing a careful count of actual stock on hand.

   Notification of Receipt of Orders.   In this example of notification of receipt of orders the return of the card to the computer system as input does not necessarily add any additional data, although it does signal that an event has occurred. In this case the event is the receipt of goods into stock. The computer system processes a stock master file, updating it with debits, that is, items issued out of stock. When the quantity on hand falls below a certain predetermined level, the system automatically generates an order to be sent to the supplier or factory. At the same time, for each item on the order, a card is punched containing identification information and details of the order. The cards are interpreted and held, perhaps at the warehouse where the goods will be delivered. When a delivery is received, the appropriate cards are pulled and sent back to the computer system to trigger an update to the corresponding master file fields. Additional data need be added to the card only when the quantity delivered differs from the quantity ordered, as in the case of a part delivery, for example.

Payroll Information for Hourly Paid Workers.   Figure 17.3 illustrates the use of a mark-sense card for payroll information. The punched cards are produced in the usual way, taking employee identification from the payroll master file. They are interpreted and distributed to the supervisors. At the end of the week, data on overtime hours worked, vacation time, and so on, are marked on the cards by hand. An off-line mark-sense reader reads the cards and automatically punches the data. The cards are then fed into the payroll input stream in the usual way. One marked character occupies three punch positions on the card; a maximum of 26 characters can thus be marked. It is fairly simple, however, to continue marking on the reverse side of the card, for a total of 52 columns. The deck then has to be fed through the mark-sense reader-punch twice to punch all columns.

Optical Character Recognition Document.   Figure 17.4 illustrates an optical character recognition-document. In this example descriptive details are printed in optical characters by the printer using a special print chain. The documents are printed two-up on continuous stationery, which is burst later for distribution to meter readers. The readings are marked onto the card on the right-hand portion, and the documents are read directly into the computer via an optical document reader. In this case the alphanumeric descriptive data is for human use only, the computer system requiring only the code line along the bottom and the marked meter readings. Although it is not evident from the monochrome illustration of Figure 17.4, most of the document is printed in light blue and light red, which are dropout colors invisible

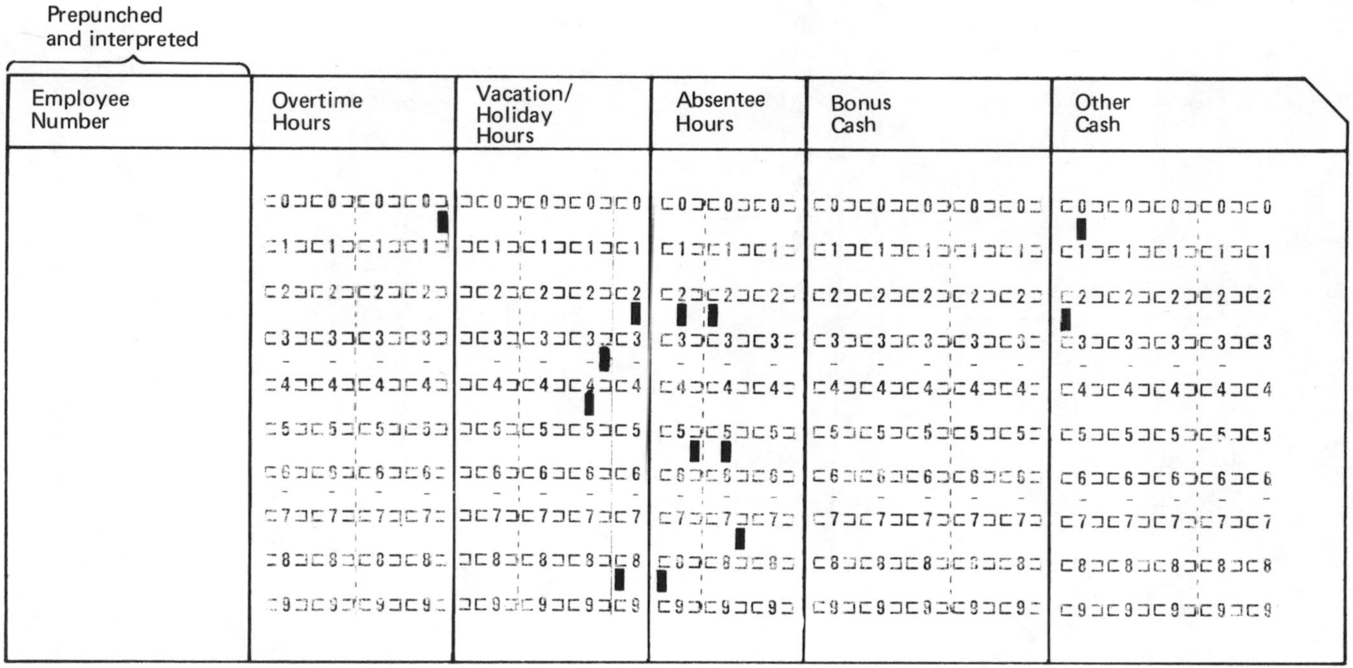

Fig. 17.3 Payroll mark-sense turnaround card

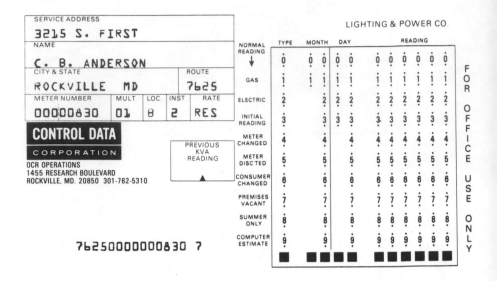

Fig. 17.4 Optical character recognition–optical mark reading turnaround document (Courtesy Control Data Corp.)

to the optical reader. The squares along the bottom right are timing marks for the reader.

DESIGN CONSIDERATIONS

The advantage of turnaround documents over the more usual form-filling transcription methods of input lies in the following savings due to elimination of hand writing and hand keying:

1. Faster preparation in the user area
2. Reduction or elimination of the need for keypunching
3. Faster input to the system resulting in more up-to-date files
4. Fewer errors

Other costs will be incurred, however. Using the card output punch on-line to the main-frame computer is very slow and therefore expensive in comparison with the speeds and processing costs of third-generation computers. The line printer, although faster than the card punch, is still slow compared to other computer peripherals such as tapes and disks. In addition there are the costs of interpreting and handling cards or of bursting and distributing paper forms. Savings actually realized may therefore be more in speed of input than in money.

Painstaking design and testing of procedures for the user area is essential. It is especially important if the staff who will be expected to handle the forms—for example, warehousemen, truck drivers, or factory workers—are not accustomed to paperwork. "Do not bend, fold, or mutilate" warnings may be insufficient if the environment is not suitable for documents that must be processed by computer, which could well be the case in a factory or outdoors. Turnaround documents may not be the solution. Even in relatively suitable conditions card trays, trolleys, and other appropriate storage and handling equipment should always be supplied.

PUNCHED CARDS

The system designer should always consider using an *off-line* magnetic tape-to-card device for producing turnaround punched cards. The tape can be formatted from a computer program, then taken offline to punch the cards. The savings in computer time would be considerable. Also it may be possible to use an interpreting punch, so that interpretation of the cards for human use is not an extra step. If the volume of turnaround cards is high, this solution should always be considered; if the volume is low, there is probably little justification for turnaround cards in the first place.

If variable data is to be handwritten directly onto the card as in Figure 17.2 (quantity on hand), a designer from the company supplying the cards should be consulted. Some keypunch machines have mechanisms that obscure part of the card while it is being punched, making it necessary to insure that the operator can see the handwritten field when the card is in the right position for punching. Moreover, care must be taken that after the holes are punched, it is still possible to read the original entry; otherwise there will be no way to verify it.

OPTICAL CHARACTER RECOGNITION
AND OPTICAL MARK READING

Design of optical character recognition and optical mark reading documents is the specialist's province, not to be undertaken by a novice. Some of the factors that have to be specified are as follows:

1. Document size, trim, and skew tolerance
2. Paper weight, thickness, opacity, and color
3. Ink luminance and density
4. Positioning, density, tolerances of recognition, and timing marks

Not every high-speed computer line printer can produce documents of acceptable quality. Chain printers are preferable to drum printers (see Chapter 4).

Design is obviously a highly technical exercise. There are three sets of resources to call on for help: the printer supplying the forms, the manufacturer of the line printer, and the manufacturer of the optical reader. All three will be needed in specifying the form.

Samples of the documents should be tested under field conditions and in sufficient volumes to establish statistically meaningful error figures for document reading to ensure that the error level in live running will be one that is acceptable. It is not prudent to make a final commitment to this method until the testing is completed to satisfaction.

CHAPTER 18

Protection of Confidential Output

It is impossible to separate output security from the security of the entire system. This chapter is concerned with data confidentiality. An outline of the types of security problems facing the system designer will be given, followed by a discussion of techniques for protection of confidential output insofar as these can be considered as topics in isolation from the subject of total system security. An exhaustive discussion in the space available here is not possible. Security is becoming a specialist's subject to which a large body of literature is devoted; references to some of the more important writings in the field are given in the Bibliography.

SECURITY PROBLEMS FACING THE DESIGNER

The first problem is to determine what data or information in the system, if any, is confidential and its value to the company; or, put another way, its potential destructive value should it fall into the wrong hands. Information that is considered extremely valuable within the company and worth large expenditures on data processing to obtain, may be of no interest, or already available to, an outsider; it cannot therefore be considered confidential. An example is *The New York Times* Information Bank; it contains data available to anyone from any large public library, its value within the computer system being only in its ease of access. On the other hand data of no interest within the organization could have a very high value to the competition; for example, details of unfruitful lines of research that have been abandoned.

221

The second problem is to evaluate the degree of risk and the consequences of a breach of security in order to determine the extent of the protection required. The likelihood of an earthquake in New York City, to take an extreme example, is so low that it can be disregarded and no precautions taken. The possibility of a computer operator taking a look at the payroll printout to see what his boss is earning, to take an example at the opposite end of the spectrum, is so high as to be almost a certainty. On the other hand the results of the earthquake would be infinitely more serious. The expenditure on protection depends on this combination of probability and consequences. A high level of protection is indicated when *both* are high.

The third problem is to devise protective measures, balancing risk against cost against effectiveness. The first two problems require solid logical thought and realism; the last one leaves more scope for imagination. It is necessary to outthink both the fools who could unintentionally corrupt data and the smartest criminal masterminds. A password system, for example, cries out for imaginative thinking. "Open Sesame" or the user's birthdate are not only dull but also unlikely to deter an imposter for long.

GENERAL CATEGORIES OF RISK

The three general categories of risk, with examples, are summarized in Figure 18.1.

Accidental Exposure

Accidental exposure or corruption of confidential data could happen as a result of program or hardware failures, opportunist browsing when adequate controls do not exist, or a disaster requiring emergency measures that temporarily short cut security controls. The probability of occurrence depends on the physical and systems environment of the installation. The possibility of bugs in operational software, for example, always exists, the degree of risk depending on the care taken during development and testing and on the age of the system.

Whether to concentrate protective measures on prevention, detection, or recovery, and to what extent, depends on the nature of the risk. The first line of defense against bad input is prevention: basic measures such as verifying, batch controls, and check digits. Assuming that it is impossible to stop all errors before the input reaches the

Type of Risk	Examples	Relative Probability	Type of Protection
Accidental exposure	Inaccurate data due to bad input	High	Prevention, detection, recovery
	Browsing in hard-copy reports by staff	Very high if no restrictions	Prevention
	System bugs allow unauthorized on-line access	Low to medium	Detection, prevention
	Disaster requires emergency off-site processing	Low to medium	Recovery
Intentional active access	Destructive sabotage	Low	Detection, recovery, prevention
	Use of software trapdoors	Low	Prevention, detection
	Imposter gaining access through terminal	Low to medium	Prevention, detection
Intentional passive access	Browsing in hard-copy residue	Medium to high	Prevention
	Line tapping	Low	Prevention
	Electromagnetic eavesdropping	Very low	Prevention

Fig. 18.1 Confidential output risk summary

computer system, there must be methods of detecting them, primarily in the input edit program, and procedures for correction and resubmission of the transactions in question. On the other hand prevention may be impossible for "Acts of God" such as earthquakes or floods. "Detection" is of course moot. In that situation resources must be concentrated on assuring quick recovery, including insurance, backup files, alternate processing arrangements, and temporary cessation of production of confidential output until normal arrangements can be resumed.

Intentional Active Access

Intentional active access means direct tampering with hardware or software, often both. The degree of risk for ordinary commercial businesses is often low, usually negligible. The reason for this is that active access requires both expertise and money, the exception being destructive sabotage, which would not in any case expose confidential output. (Furthermore, categorizing sabotage as access may be stretching a point.) To illustrate the negligible risk it will serve to cite the case of the manager of a time-sharing bureau who offered a "reward" of $100 to anyone who could breach the security of his system via an unauthorized terminal. No one even tried. If the offer had been for, say, $25,000, it is quite likely that the reward would have been claimed not long after. The potential gain for the "intruder" must be greater than the trouble and cost of the tampering, circumstances existing in only a few businesses—perhaps more often in military and government establishments. This leads to an important maxim of computer security: *One hundred percent protection is impossible. The goal must be to make the cost of obtaining confidential data greater than the value of that data.* Money spent to raise the level of protection above that point is wasted.

Intentional Passive Access

The same principle applies to some of the methods of intentional passive access. Wiretapping, for example, requires planning and some money. More important, the interpretation of digital signals after they have been obtained needs time, money, and expertise, especially if the results are to be available in time to make good use of them. Most confidential data lose their value over a period of time. Company financial statements, for example, are of interest for "insider" stock market manipulation only until they are published; new product information is useful to a competitor only if he can copy the product and announce his imitation early enough.

The factor that elevates passive access into a potentially very dangerous security breach is that by definition it is almost impossible to detect. Nothing is missing; nothing can be seen to be wrong. A copy made does not affect the original in any way. Even knowing that it has happened is of negligible value after the fact. Active access can at least theoretically, and often practically (at least in a single-user system), be detected while it is going on in time to do something. For example, the system can be programmed to log repeated illegal passwords in time to direct a human being to the terminal where the culprit is trying to gain access by trial and error. If he has merely tapped the transmission line, there will be no signal.

For these reasons, protection against passive access must be almost entirely concentrated on prevention, rather than on detection or recovery. The security techniques for protecting confidential output that are outlined below are mostly in that category.

CLASSIFYING DATA

It is a useful first step to determine what data is confidential and to what degree. One example of a classification system, adapted from a real-life organization, is shown in Figure 18.2. There are 10 cate-

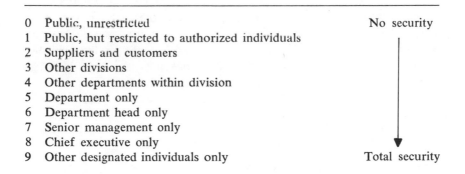

0   Public, unrestricted   No security
1   Public, but restricted to authorized individuals
2   Suppliers and customers
3   Other divisions
4   Other departments within division
5   Department only
6   Department head only
7   Senior management only
8   Chief executive only
9   Other designated individuals only   Total security

Fig. 18.2   Example of confidentiality ratings

gories ranging from unrestricted to designated individual only. Most commercial organizations will not need such a large number of categories; three or four are usually sufficient. (Military and classified government establishments are outside the scope of this discussion.)

If the classification system is a useful one, it is usually found that only a small percentage of data falls into the top security categories. As a rule of thumb these items probably should not be processed by computer at all. Examples would be personal medical details of staff that could expose an individual to risk of blackmail, or details of commercially valuable new products not otherwise protected, for example, by patent. Data at this level of sensitivity should be kept with as little documentation as possible, that is, probably only one copy (or two at most) under direct control of the individual responsible and under lock and key in a protected place.

A large portion of commercial data will require no protection at all, falling into the unrestricted classification. This is information that has no value to an outsider because it has no inherent value, because it can be obtained elsewhere, or because its value lies in its currency, which will be exhausted by the time it becomes output from a computer system.

Some information will fall into the middle categories, indicating that some degree of protection is required. This will be data that could be of value to a competitor or of detriment to the organization if it fell into the wrong hands. It is rarely possible to assign a monetary value to this kind of information, hence the classification system. Although specifying the worth of the data to the company cannot be done, the *relative* worth of different types can be determined.

When the classification is being done, it may be found that only a small proportion of the data items fall into the high priority categories. This may provide guidelines for file and output design, indicating that the small handful of sensitive items should be handled and printed separately, with high security procedures applied. Although this will keep the volume of data to be protected low, it may also call attention to what is valuable. Such a decision can be taken only in light of local circumstances.

PROTECTING BATCH OUTPUT

By batch output is meant hard-copy reports coming off the line printer in the computer room. (Data transmitted to a remote location before printing will be considered below under the subject of protecting on-line information.) There are four areas where protection is required. They are in the computer room, in the data control section, during transport, and in the user offices. Each will be discussed in turn.

The Computer Room

The point at which confidential information becomes output in the computer room is when printing begins. Up until that time, while it was on magnetic files or being processed by the computer, it was relatively secure from prying eyes. Now there are two groups of people who might be able to read it: authorized computer room staff and unauthorized outsiders who have gained entry to the computer room. Little need be said about the latter group, because ordinary access control procedures that should be in operation anyway will easily exclude them. No unaccompanied unauthorized person should have the opportunity to get into the computer room or even into the corridors leading to it. Staff who are allowed inside should be clearly designated, and all others should be challenged on sight.

Protecting confidential data from the eyes of computer room staff, which probably means computer operators in most cases, is a different problem, however. First, let it be said that it is difficult to imagine circumstances in which operators could not be trusted to see any output. It is not likely that they will have time to study it, and good quality control demands that they be able to at least scan it. In extreme circumstances, however, there are several simple procedures that can be applied. The first is to suppress printout on the top copy of the report, which with most printers can be done by removing the ribbon. The second is to have a senior manager present while printing is being done, perhaps the user to whom the report belongs. It is *not* recommended that a security guard be posted beside the printer, as has been done in some installations; the presence of a person unknowledgeable about computer room procedures is worse than useless. Neither of these steps will stop a curious or criminally inclined operator from obtaining his own copy of the printout unless careful control is kept of the number of copies of the forms and of computer usage through the software and operator logs. These are matters of good operations management generally rather than security in particular.

The Data Control Section

Much the same kind of remark can be made about protection of the printout while it is being processed in the data control area. It is necessary to ensure that all copies are accounted for and that unauthorized outsiders are excluded from the area. If necessary, the senior manager who watched over the printing can do the same for the de-collating, bursting, and binding steps. There is, however, one potentially weak spot in data control that is often overlooked in even the most security conscious installations. That is the disposal of the one-time carbon when it is used. The printing is usually quite legible on the carbon for anyone determined enough to try to read it. Yet it is dis-posed of as ordinary waste paper, the single most fertile source for professional industrial spies. Use of a paper shredder or a waste com-pactor is the most straightforward way to close this loophole, or the "burn bag" of military installations can be used.

Transportation and Distribution

Transportation and distribution of confidential reports also re-quire only the application of common sense. Very confidential reports, those in the top security classification, should be treated as if they were cash. If procedures already exist in the company for the transport of large sums of money in cash, these can be easily adopted for the printout as well. Locked boxes, security guards, armored vehicles, and the usual associated procedures can be used. Some experts consider that transportation by armed security couriers is the most safe method; others regard the United States Post Office as the best, among them diamond merchants, who regularly send packets of diamonds worth vast sums by ordinary first-class post. This can be expensive for large volumes of data, however. Copy control, signatures of authorized per-sons on receipt of the output, and a double check on receipt will round out the procedures required for almost all confidential data.

The User Areas

Security in the user areas depends largely on local circumstances. The most basic precaution is to keep the printout under lock and key except when it is actually in use. Rigid precautions in the computer area are ludicrous if the manager leaves the report on his desk in an unattended office while he goes out to lunch. Disposal after use is again a potentially weak area. If the information still has value when the time comes to get rid of it, a paper shredder is the most obvious answer.

Finally, mention should be made of what has been called the "null message" technique. This was first discussed in Chapter 5. Ap-plied to hard-copy printout, this is the technique of filling all blank spaces with randomly generated, meaningless characters. The printout would thus be nonsense to a casual scan. The user can be given a template that, when placed over the page, obscures the nonsense characters and allows the meaningful data to be read.

PROTECTING ON-LINE OUTPUT

It is useful to approach the subject of on-line output as we did the last one, that is, by considering the physical location of the confidential information at various stages in its life cycle. This breaks down into the areas of inside the computer, transmission over public or private lines, display on a visual display unit, and hard-copy remote output. Data within the computer, being processed, will be dealt with quickly because it is a problem that is not within the scope of this book. Suffice it to say that the risk is usually less than is thought; and that the most likely method of illegal access is through a remote terminal, which can be controlled with good terminal lockup procedures and, particularly, with well-designed monitoring and logging software.

Public or Private Transmission

Transmission of data from central computer (or for that matter, into it) can be local, within the building, or remote, over longer distances. Local transmission can use private, dedicated lines that are as safe from tampering as the building itself. Security of data being sent over longer distances poses greater problems. The best method of protection is to encode the data before transmission and decode it on receipt. A summary of the main methods of doing so is given here.

The methods of encoding or encrypting data with which the most work has been done for computer usage are substitution, transposition, and addition. Substitution codes are the type, often developed by children, in which every A is replaced by a B, every B by a C, and so on. Transposition involves rearranging the data according to some predetermined pattern. Addition codes are keys that are used to transform the data in some way by adding, subtracting, multiplying, dividing, or some other operation. The strength or weakness of any coding system lies in the length of the key used. The more often the same method is repeated, that is, the shorter the key, the easier it is to break the code. The only virtually unbreakable code is one that uses a randomly generated key that is as long as the message to be transmitted and is never repeated. The code is unbreakable as long as the key is kept secret, of course.

There are two practical methods of encoding and decoding data within a computer system: with software or with hardware, that is, a pair of "black-boxes," one at each end of the line.

A programmed technique is vulnerable to disclosure of the logic used, that is, in effect, disclosure of the key. Otherwise, its effectiveness depends on the encryption method used. A possible difficulty is that it is necessary to have programmable memory at the receiving end to decode the message.

There are a number of encryption devices for use with computer transmission equipment on the market. They can be kept locked with only authorized individuals in possession of the keys. The encoding key can be changed by opening the device and resetting it. The advantages of electronic coding units are that they are relatively inexpensive, very easy to use, and very secure, provided always that the key is changed frequently.

Several general points need to be made about the use of cryptographic techniques, whatever method is used. The first is that it is necessary to avoid developing in the encoded message bit patterns that would be taken by the transmission equipment to be control characters. It is thus necessary either to use a method in which this is impossible or to screen the encrypted message and transform "illegal" characters. The second point is that the use of nulls (inserting garbage at random intervals in the transmission) greatly improves the security of any encryption technique. One method of doing this is to send out randomly generated noise during gaps in normal transmission. Finally, it must be emphasized that the encryption technique is only as good as the other security procedures that surround it. The effort of encoding data for transmission is wasted if the user leaves a copy of the report "in clear" where anyone could pick it up.

There is obviously a great deal more that can be said about the technicalities of encryption techniques. A great deal of work is being done on the subject. Readers who wish to pursue the subject further are referred to Canning (December, 1973, and January 1974), Skatrud (1969), and Van Tassel (1969) in the Bibliography as a starting point.

Visual Display

After transmission, the data may next be displayed on a screen. Because this is transitory, leaving no permanent record behind, protecting confidentiality need not be difficult. Unauthorized outsiders must be kept away from the vicinity of the screen, preferably kept out of the room. Hoods can be installed around the screens to prevent casual viewing by bystanders.

Hard-Copy Remote Output

The protection of hard-copy data after transmission demands the same procedures as for any other hard-copy output. Methods for doing this have already been outlined. One point remains to be added, however, which is that there should be some verification before transmission begins that the individual attending the equipment at the receiving end is authorized to do so. Methods of doing this include the use of passwords if two-way transmission is possible or if not, identification over other lines of communication such as the telephone.

SUMMARY

This discussion of practical methods of protecting the confidentiality of computer-processed information has been limited to data in its output mode. As was said at the beginning of the chapter, security is a very wide subject in which much work is being done at present. It is thus impossible to attempt to give the last word on the subject in a book such as this. It is hoped that what has been done here is to give a starting point for further study to those readers who are, or will become, responsible for this aspect of data processing in their installations.

CHAPTER 19

Software for Report Production

Software is a program or a set of programs that is generalized to serve more than one user. It can be bought more or less off the shelf from the computer manufacturer or from an independent software supplier. The type of software we are concerned with in this chapter is designed for the production of computer output. There are two major categories for this purpose. The first is software for use with graph plotters, usually written for a particular device; these were discussed in Part Four. The second type of package, that under discussion in this chapter, is for output reports on the line printer. A separate chapter is devoted to this subject because of the large number of such software packages available and because of the almost universal potential market for them—every commercial installation that has a line printer is a possible customer for a packaged report generator.

The input for a report generator is one or more computer files, either tape or disk, *plus* a set of parameter records describing the input files and specifying the output required. Some software will generate and maintain a dictionary of file descriptions so that these need be written only once. The parameters for the output describe the headings, layout, and contents of the report desired, plus specification of options to be taken, depending on the features offered by the package. These could include selecting only certain records for printing, various arithmetic operations, summary totals to be printed, constants to be added, and so on.

Some of these software packages operate in a "load-and-go" mode, taking the parameter records, often punched cards, as direct input (see Figure 19.1 for an illustration). Others are precompilers (as in Figure

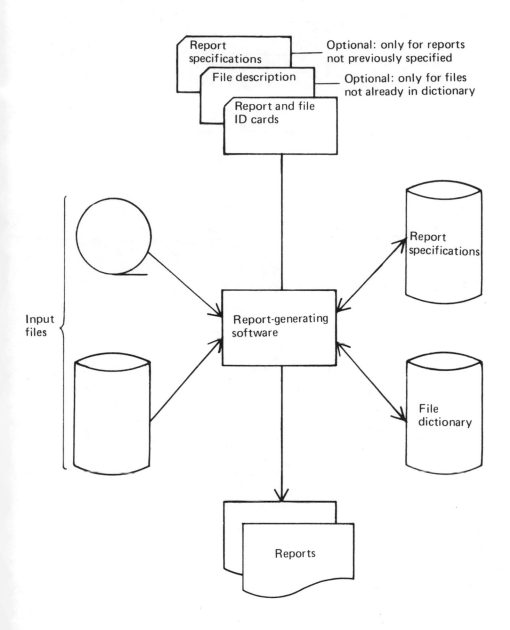

Fig. 19.1   Load-and-go dictionary-driven software

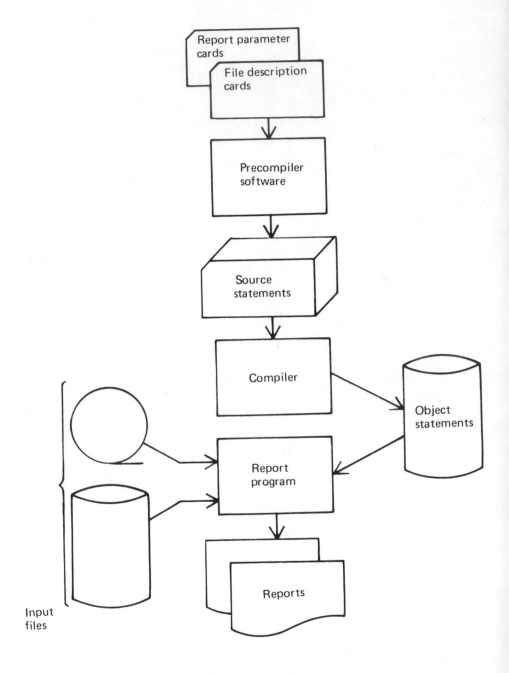

Fig. 19.2 Precompiler software

234

19.2) in which the software output consists of source language statements that are then compiled in the usual way. Still other packages are themselves compilers, producing object-language instructions for loading and execution (as in Figure 19.3). Summary information about just a few of the packages on the market will be found in Appendix A.

The features incorporated into these commercial software packages vary in scope from the most basic to very complex. At one end of the scale are simple card-to-print utilities for producing mock-up reports. These can be quite useful for user presentations at early stages of the project, as was pointed out in Chapter 5. At the other extreme are the very large packages offering multifile processing with hierarchical record selection and remote terminal interface, for example. Some are more than report generators, being capable of creating and maintaining files as well. These are more properly called "generalized file processors," or "information retrieval systems," rather than report generators.

There is a wide range of prices, too. Outright purchase prices vary from a few hundred dollars to upward of $20,000. Monthly rental rates are as low as $60 for one package and as high as $800 for another. Some are only sold outright, whereas others are only available on license or lease; many can be had either way. It is well to point out here that a comparison on price alone can be misleading. Some software houses include full installation support, training, and maintenance in the price; others send only a deck of cards and an instruction manual. More will be said about evaluating those relative factors later in the chapter.

ADVANTAGES AND DISADVANTAGES

The major advantage of using report-generating software is reduction of programmer effort. The steps of detailed logic flowcharting, coding, and testing are all virtually eliminated. This has two major effects. The first is a potentially very considerable saving in programming costs. The second is a significantly faster response to users' requests for new or modified reports. This latter factor is particularly important in installations in which a large portion of the requests for reports are on a one-off basis, that is, a particular report required only once or at most at irregular and infrequent intervals. The user can get his output much sooner than if a new program had to be coded and tested, and the cost to the company is much less.

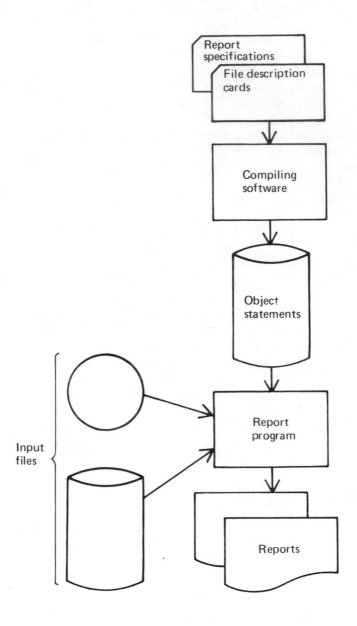

Fig. 19.3 Compiler software

236

This does not mean, however, that all programmer effort is necessarily eliminated. For a new report, someone must specify and code the parameters cards for the software. To do so requires a certain amount of training. There is always the possibility of an error in the parameter cards, meaning that a large amount of computer time may be wasted in printing a useless report, or at the very least that some debugging will be required. The software companies offering these packages are acutely aware of this problem, and most of them have taken pains to make their instruction manuals as clear as possible and their input specification forms as foolproof as they can. Some go so far as to aim for "user-oriented" input statements so that the programmer is not required. How successful the user will be in specifying his own reports depends on his attitudes and aptitudes. Experience has shown that accountants and personnel managers adapt more easily to the idea than warehouse and factory staff, for example, although this is not true in all organizations.

Another possible problem is that the software will impose restrictions on the content and format of the report. How severe the limitations are will depend almost entirely on the software chosen. Selecting the best possible package to meet the installation's requirements, both present and future, will be discussed later. Even with the most versatile package, however, the problem could range from having to compromise on the layout to being unable to produce a certain new report at all. There are bound to be disappointments if the salesman's claims are taken too literally. There is no reason to suppose that software will be able to handle all output requirements; its use can often be justified even when only a part of the reporting requirements are met.

Another objection often raised against the use of software is its inefficient utilization of the hardware. In many cases this is a false assumption. A load-and-go processor must be generalized, which means that some, or even much, of its code is unexecuted in any one run, and that the portions that are executed may not be written for peak efficiency for all occasions. Compilers and precompilers are designed to overcome this objection because of their "optimizing" abilities, but then extra computer time is required for the compilation. There are two very strong counters to these arguments.

The first is the fact that printing time, on the slowest device in the configuration, will occupy most of the processing time. This would be true whether a software package or a handwritten program were used. All of the CPU time will be overlapped by file input/output, particularly printing; inefficient utilization of the CPU will be a negligible factor in the overall throughput. The second defense is a practical one; a comparison test under operational conditions can show whether the software runs faster or slower than hand coding for the same output, and surprisingly the software often wins. This kind of a test is called a "benchmark" and will be discussed in more detail later.

Other possible pros and cons are in the areas of implementation support, training, documentation, and maintenance. It is unwise to generalize here because the quality and quantity of this support varies between software houses, ranging from nonexistent to excellent. A package that is little more than a utility program will probably not include anything more than a few pages of notes and this may well be all that is needed. A larger and more complex system needs more support. Having to debug and maintain someone else's programs can be very difficult, even when the documentation is good. If the documentation is poor or nonexistent, the software experiment can end in disaster. Many software houses offer a full support service, either included in the purchase price or as a separate agreement. Some even extend to a 24-hour emergency debugging service. If such support is required, its quality is all important for successful use of the software.

There is one final drawback to the use of this kind of software that should be mentioned. Its seriousness depends on the environment and experience of the installation. It is the "not invented here syndrome," that is, resistance among data processing staff to the use of any programs not written by themselves. If this resistance is strong and entrenched, even the best software faces failure. Software houses counter with a double-edged argument. First they say that their packages do the complicated routines and leave the easy work for the installation's staff, a point of view that might endear itself to company management but is unlikely to be met with joy among the programmers. The about-face point of view is that the software does the routine, boring jobs and leaves the analysts and programmers free to work on more advanced and experimental systems. This is probably closer to the truth for report generators; most print programs are lengthy to write but not particularly challenging for experienced programmers. If the software purchase allows staff to be freed for new projects, their objections in this area can often be met.

SOFTWARE SELECTION

From this point on we will assume that a decision has been made to look into the possibility of acquiring a report generator for a specific installation. The project will have many of the characteristics of a small-scale feasibility study. The steps required are as follows:

1. Locating "possibles"
2. Collecting information about them
3. Establishing selection criteria
4. Discarding nonstarters and drawing up a short list
5. Evaluating in depth, possibly including a technical evaluation
6. Reporting results for a final decision
7. Finalizing contract details
8. Implementing system

Each of these steps will be discussed, but throughout it should be borne in mind that the time and effort invested in this project should be in proportion to the importance of the contemplated acquisition. A dollar-a-day print utility does not merit the kind of full-scale study necessary for an on-line information retrieval system interfacing with a data base management information system. The guidelines given here are for something in between. The steps recommended can be contracted or expanded to suit the circumstances.

Locating Possible Packages

Finding report generators being offered for sale need not be difficult as long as the goal is not to identify every single one; that is a task akin to painting the George Washington Bridge, where as soon as you get to one end, you have to start over at the other. New packages and enhancements to existing ones are being announced every week. The main sources of information will be the technical literature and the computer manufacturer. Both should be tapped.

There is more software currently available for IBM 360/370 machines than for any other, which is not surprising. Users of IBM will find a wide choice of report generators. Most other machines are covered as well, although if difficulty is encountered, it might be useful to approach a software house offering an otherwise suitable package about the possibility of having it converted. As a general rule the smaller the manufacturer, the more likely he is to be familiar with the software offered for his machines by software houses, and the more willing he will be to advise and assist in finding it. This source of help should be sought from the start.

Although the body of technical literature on this subject is enormous, a scan of the major periodicals for, say, the last six months will not take long. If they are not available in the installation, most large business libraries will have adequate collections. Software catalogs and information services can also be very useful. In an emergency a consultant can be called in for advice, but his services could well be more expensive than can be justified unless he is also undertaking an evaluation of the software against the installation's stated requirements.

Collecting Information

A phone call or a letter to the suppliers of the packages identified will elicit quantities of sales literature and possibly a few salesmen. The salesmen can be ignored at this stage; they will be happy to come back later if their software passes the initial tests.

Some nonstarters can be eliminated at once, possibly from the advertisement or the listing in the software catalog, if they are not in the right price range or not implemented on the installation's hardware. How many dropouts there are will depend on the rigidity of these initial criteria and whether the hardware is IBM, as was pointed out earlier.

Establishing Selection Criteria

This step deserves close attention because time and care invested now can save much wasted effort. The first task is to set down a list of those requirements for the software that are essential. What is essential in one installation will not be in another, so no rigid rules can be established. The kinds of things that might go on such a list are shown in Figure 19.4. Minimum hardware configuration and operating system

---

Minimum hardware configuration
Operating system
Number of input files
Record extraction capability
Number of summary levels
Ease of use
How soon available
Installation support given
Maintenance support given
Price and terms

Fig. 19.4   Basic selection criteria for report software

required for the software will be on most lists, as could be the programming language. The maximum number and type of input files accepted by the report generator, the type and extent of record extraction features, and the number of levels of summary totals on the output are usually major criteria as well. Ease of use might be important in one situation, for example, if junior programmers or user clerical staff will be specifying parameters, but not in another. The same applies to how fast the package can be installed and how much help the supplier will give. Similarly, purchase or rental price might or might not be critical. Other lists might have other criteria, such as, for example, geographical location of the supplier (related to support services), performance of mathematical calculations, or exits for own coding.

Establishing this list of criteria cannot be done in a vacuum. In some cases a particular application or set of processing requirements has developed, and this has initiated a software project. If so, the feasibility study or other project work to date will supply the guidelines. On the other hand there may be no specific application area to match the software against, but rather a generally felt need for "something to help out." In that case the best course is to find or invent sample output report specifications, the kind of job the software will be called on to do. These should obviously be the demanding jobs—those more complex reports that are, or will become, typical of the user's requirements—rather than the uncomplicated ones. The list of selection criteria can then be written to eliminate any software that would be totally unsuitable, leaving for a short list only those that are capable of producing the type of output required.

In-Depth Study

At this point the selection exercise could end. This would happen if only one package was left on the list, or even if none were left. In the latter case the options are to forget software and do it in-house, to make the criteria less stringent and start again, or to approach one or more software houses about the possibility of modifying their packages to suit. If only one package is left, the decision becomes yes or no. If the decision is no, the same options listed above apply; if yes, it is still wise to check on some of the further evaluation criteria discussed below, especially those having to do with the supplier and the contract.

The purpose of the in-depth study is to reduce the choices to one by eliminating the others on the short list. This in-depth study may not, in fact, be any more extensive than that of the first round of selection; it will become less as the packages left on the list become fewer and the processing they will have to do when operational in the installation becomes simpler. Having passed the major requirements, the packages still left will now have to be tested to find the one that gives the best value for the money.

Further information may now be required. Detailed package documentation, sales calls and formal presentations, visits to other installations using the package, and demonstrations are all ways of finding out more. The information gathering will be easier and faster if detailed lists of questions are drawn up. Categories of information required follow.

1. The supplier
2. Package history
3. Major trade-offs
4. Package features
5. Operating requirements
6. Documentation
7. Training and installation support
8. Contract terms

Comments will be made on each of these.

The reputation and business integrity of the supplier are important. Regardless of legal contracts, the success of software acquisition depends on the mutual trust and goodwill between the supplier and the customer. The software house should be willing to give information about its history and operation, as well as names of other clients for references. These can be followed up with a phone call or a letter, if not with a visit. The size and age of the company are important, although a small, young software house is not necessarily to be avoided. In fact, a more well-established organization may be less keen for business and less eager to please than a younger one. The customer should avoid doing business in a situation in which he will represent a major portion of the supplier's turnover; this is not healthy for either the customer or the supplier. If it will be necessary to depend on the supplier for maintenance and other support over a period of time, there should be some assurance that he is financially stable and not apt to go out of business at any moment. Recent history has taught that even some of the most reputable and well-established data processing service companies can suddenly disappear or withdraw their products. Thus any contract should cover the possibility of the supplier going out of business or otherwise relinquishing his rights to the software and its support.

The history of the package includes who developed it and why, and who owns what rights in it. For example, if the people who originated and wrote the software work for the company that is selling it are available to support their product, it can be assumed with some degree of assurance that the technical staff sent to do the implementation and training will know what they are about.

The major trade-offs comprise those items previously listed as basic selection criteria. These should now be verified. Some packages are shown as being suitable for a certain configuration or operating system, for example, when in fact what is meant is that the supplier is willing to convert to a desired version. Exactly what is included in the price and what is not should also be established at this time.

At this stage the package features can be investigated in more detail. The way to do this is to prepare a feature comparison check list showing what each package can do. This may require careful study of the documentation supplied and consultations with salesmen; what is a "matrix format" to one software house may be "multiline format" to another and what the first sees as "simultaneous multifile comparison and retrieval" might be "coordinated input files with record scan supporting repeating data groups" to the second; or then again, it might not. Actual samples of their output will also help.

An example of a feature comparison checklist for report generators is shown in Figure 19.5. It is designed so that two or three competing packages can be compared side by side, with the entry beside each feature item filled in with "yes," "no," a number, or a few words of description. Use of such a layout will also help to ensure that all the information about each package has been obtained. In some cases not all of these features will be required; in others extra ones may have to be added. Study of the suppliers' documentation may suggest other features to be put on the list.

The documentation that will be supplied with the package should be inspected. This is particularly important if maintenance is to be done in-house, in which case completeness, quality, and ease of use are essential. A check should also be made on whether the material is copyright, and if it is, on whether the purchaser will be allowed to make copies for internal use in his organization. Without prior permission copies cannot be made of any documentation that is copyright.

The software house should be willing to give details of the training and implementation support they will supply and its cost. Some com-

Package name:
Supplier name and address:
Name of salesman:
Telephone number:

Minimum configuration required
Programming language
Operating system, version and level
Types of files handled
    tape
    disk, sequential
    disk, indexed
    disk, random
    disk, VISAM
Maximum number of files
Types of records handled
    fixed and variable
    undefined
    blocked and unblocked
Types of fields handled
    alphanumeric
    packed
    binary
Types of record selection criteria
    max fields per record
    max record types
    constants
    calculated
    nth item sampling
    simultaneous/multiple
    matching
    exclusion factors
    accumulation of retrieval statistics
Arithmetic functions
    add/subtract
    multiply/divide
    rounding
    square root
    standard deviation
    averages
    record/field counts
    cross-footing
Sorting capability
Own-code exits

Maximum output reports per pass
Output to tape or disk
Output to spooler
Levels of summary totals
Noncolumnar reports
Editing capabilities
Number of title lines
Number of heading lines
Spacing options
Default options
Other output features
Error procedures
    fatal diagnostics
    default choices
    handling of data exceptions
    abort routines
Dictionary features
    by file
    by record
    by report
    override options
Parameter specification
    by whom done
    number form types
    forms supplied

Fig. 19.5 Example of feature comparison checklist

panies run public training courses for users and potential users of their software. This can be a convenient and inexpensive way of gaining detailed knowledge of the system, as well as being a convenience for training new staff throughout the life of the software. From the buyer's point of view, the best kind of implementation support is open ended, with the supplier's staff working on site to install the system and staying until a successful acceptance period has elapsed. This may be included in the purchase price or negotiated separately. Other schemes give a fixed number of man-days of support, with further help charged at a daily rate.

Suppliers who are under serious consideration should be requested to give a copy of their standard contract for inspection, whether the acquisition is a purchase or a lease. This document should be studied and amendments negotiated before a final decision is reached. Some basic guidelines for contract negotiation follow.

1. Review of the contract by a legal expert
2. Negotiation with only one person (with the most senior executive available)
3. Documentation of all verbal agreements
4. Contract specification of everything that is to be included (If the contract does not actually contain the package specifications, it should reference them)
5. Announcement of a final decision only after the contract has been signed by both parties

The Technical Evaluation

A technical evaluation tests the operational efficiency of the software, usually in comparison with similar software and other ways of obtaining the same results. With report generators this usually takes the form of a benchmark, with each alternative method used to produce the same output, and the times and costs compared.

A benchmark needs to be carefully planned if the results are to be meaningful. It may require large amounts of computer time, and it will certainly use up staff time. Benchmarks are done more often than is justified because they usually are fun. If the supplier will grant a trial period of use of the package, or if he will give guarantees, or if the software is in use at other installations where its efficiency and quality can be determined, a benchmark is not called for. If on the other hand the software is very complex, if it has not been on the market long enough to get reports from other users, and if it represents a large cash outlay for the buyer, then a technical evaluation should be considered.

Specifications of the output to be produced should be drawn up carefully and agreed to by all concerned as in any other systems project. The output called for should be typical of the kinds of reports that will be regularly called for in the installation, but it should be chosen to test all the major features of the software. Several different output reports may be needed to do this.

Let us take a typical example of a benchmark testing a report generator versus hand coding in COBOL. The specifications for several reports are written, as described above. One copy is turned over to an experienced COBOL programmer in the installation and one copy given to the software supplier who assigns a programmer experienced in using the software. The COBOL programmer writes and debugs his programs; the software house programmer writes and debugs his control cards. Each is timed. Then both the COBOL programs and the software are run on the same computer under the same operating system using the same input files, and the results are compared. Comparisons can include the following:

1. Coding time
2. Compilation time
3. Execution time
4. Memory required
5. Appearance of the finished reports

The timing figures can be converted to costs by applying standard rates for programmer and computer time. Adjustments may be needed to take into account data preparation time for the programs and control cards, stationery, and other supplies, and factors such as the possibility of saving COBOL coding time by copying file definitions from a library.

The figures obtained from the benchmark can be used further for a formal cost-benefit analysis. To do this the expected work load that could be taken over by the software must be known. The savings in programmer time and cost, and savings in computer time, if any, have to be balanced against the cost of the software. The usual life span of such a system is conventionally taken to be either five or seven years, so if the software is offered on an outright purchase, the price can be divided by the number of years chosen. For leased software the annual cost is used. Extras such as maintenance must also be added in if they have not been included. Maintenance costs for hand-coded programs can be assumed to be between 10 and 20 percent of development cost per year for the same time period unless installation experience dictates otherwise.

Implementation

The implementation of a report generator is not complicated. Unlike some other types of software, there is no need to build master files, and therefore a large part of the implementation effort that must be made for full-scale applications systems disappears. Compilation and cataloging of the software onto the installation's library, including checkout and tune up, can usually be accomplished very quickly.

There will then be a settling-in period while installation staff are trained and gain familiarity with the use of the software (if this has not already taken place). The biggest potential problems are those of software that is not adequately debugged and possible lack of compatibility with the installation's operating system or files. If either problem is serious, it probably means that the evaluation was not done properly. It can also mean a failure on the part of the supplier. He should be willing to stand by his product (figuratively if not literally) and provide full assistance during the shakedown period. Some suppliers offer a trial period of use at very low cost; others depend on the results of benchmarks or acceptance tests. The contract should include provision for cancellation on demand if the product proves unsatisfactory within a trial period, say, two or three months. Longer notification for termination on either side will usually be required after that time.

SUMMARY

Report generators are a category of packaged software that has earned itself a continuing market. A wide variety of packages offering many levels of complexity are available. They are very useful in environments in which a high proportion of the reporting requirements are one time, but they can also give cost savings when used for periodic reports. If the evaluation and selection are done with careful planning and intelligent analysis, a report generator can be a useful acquisition.

APPENDIX A

Report Generators

Report generators are software packages that relieve the programmer of at least some of the effort of writing code to produce output reports. The programmer, systems analyst, or in some cases the user specifies the report requirements for content, headings, arithmetic, subtotaling, and so on, as parameter cards that feed the software. Some software packages will build their own data dictionaries, or libraries; others require that the description of the input file and the records on it be submitted with the other parameter cards.

Only some of the dozens of report generators on the market are listed here. Further details can be supplied by the supplier named here, or software catalogs or the technical literature can be consulted for the names of others.

Package Name	Supplier	Hardware	Type
Argus	Atlas Van Lines 1212 St. George Rd. P.O. Box 509 Evansville, Ind. 47701	IBM 360/370	Parameter-driven load and go
Culprit III	Cullinane Corporation One Boston Place Boston, Mass. 02180	IBM 360/370 UNIVAC Ser. 70	Parameter-driven load and go
DS/3	System Development Corp. 2500 Colarado Ave. Santa Monica, Calif. 90406	IBM 369/370	Dictionary-driven on-line inquiry
DYL-250 DYL-260	Dylakor Computer Systems, Inc. 2222 Corinth Ave. Los Angeles, Calif. 90064	IBM 360/370	Parameter-driven load and go

Package Name	Supplier	Hardware	Type
Easyout	M. H. McKinney 1213 Meal Pickett College Station, Texas 77840	IBM 360/370	Parameter-driven compiler
General Retrieval System	Program Products, Inc. 20 Old Turnpike Rd. Nanuet, N.Y. 10954	IBM 360 Burroughs RCA UNIVAC GE CDC PDP-10	Dictionary-driven load and go
Information Quick (IQ)	The Management Group, Inc. 393 Totten Pond Rd. Waltham, Mass. 02154		Parameter-driven precompiler
Margen	Randolph Computer Corp. 537 Steamboat Rd. Greenwich, Conn. 06830	IBM 360/370	Parameter-driven compiler
Preview	System Implementation Corp. 18 East 48th St. New York, N.Y. 10017	IBM 360	Card-to-print utility (creates sample output)
Qwick Qwery	C A C I 12011 San Vicente Blvd. Los Angeles, Calif. 90049	IBM 360 GE 635-625 CDC 3150, 6600 UNIVAC 1108 XDS Sigma 5	Dictionary-driven compiler
Report Creation System (RCS)	McDonnell Douglas Automation P.O. Box 516 St. Louis, Mo. 63166	IBM 360/370 RCA Spectra 70 RCA System 2, 3, 6, 7	Dictionary-driven compiler
Report Expeditor (REX)	Godfrey Systems, Inc. P.O. Box 461 San Rafael, Calif. 94902	UNIVAC 1005	Parameter-driven compiler
Report Service-Very Prompt (RSVP)	National Computing Industries 6075 Roswell Rd. NE Atlanta, Ga. 30328	IBM 360/370	Parameter-driven load and go
Special Report Generator (SRG)	Management Science American, Inc. 580 Sylvan Ave. Englewood Cliffs, N.J. 07632	IBM 360/370 Burroughs B3500/4700	Parameter-driven load and go

APPENDIX B

Graphics and Plotting Software

This appendix contains outlines of a selection of software packages for producing graphics. It is divided into two sections, software for graphics from the line printer, and software for graph plotters. No attempt is made here to be comprehensive; there are literally hundreds of packages and routines on the market for graphics production. The purpose of this appendix is to give the reader an overview of the types of software available. Although no publication can claim with conviction to be 100 percent comprehensive, those engaged in a search for graphics software are referred to the *ICP Quarterly,** which contains a wide selection.

Software for Graphic Output from the Line Printer

Package Name	Supplier	Hardware	Type
Autograf	Cambridge Computer Associates, Inc. 222 Alewife Brook Parkway Cambridge, Mass. 02138	IBM 360/370	Bar charts, histograms, scattergrams
Esplot	Earth Sciences Research, Inc. 133 Mt. Auburn St. Cambridge, Mass. 02138	IBM 360/370	Simulates a graph plotter; graphs and diagrams
Data Analyzer	Program Products, Inc. 20 Old Turnpike Rd. Nanuet, N.Y. 10954	IBM 360	Tabulations and bar charts

* International Computer Programs, Inc., 2506 Willowbrook Parkway, Indianapolis, Ind. 46205.

251

Package Name	Supplier	Hardware	Type
Culprit III	Cullinane Corporation One Boston Place Boston, Mass. 02108	IBM 360; RCA Spectra 70	Tabulations and bar charts
Grid	Laboratory for Computer Graphics and Spatial Analysis 520 Gund Hall Harvard University 48 Quincy Street Cambridge, Mass. 02138	IBM 370	Maps, grids, irregular- shaped polygons
Speedplot II	Pacific Software Services Co. P.O. Box 432 Bellflower, Calif. 90706	IBM 360/370	Graphs with up to six curves each
Aedplot	Softech, Inc. 391 Totten Pond Rd. Waltham, Mass. 02154	IBM 360; CP67-CMS-AED	Numerical data for two- dimensional coordinates
Three-D	California Computer Products, Inc. 2411 West LaPalma St. Anaheim, Calif. 92801	Any computer with a CalComp Digital Plotter	Three-dimen- sional per- spective view of any surface that can be expressed as a function of two variables
Datagraph	California Computer Products, Inc. 2411 West LaPalma St. Anaheim, Calif. 92801	IBM 360	Business- oriented graphs, bar charts, and histograms
Flowgen/F	California Computer Products, Inc. 2411 West LaPalma St. Anaheim, Calif. 92810	Any computer with a CalComp Plotter	Flowcharts from Fortran source programs

Documentation Standards for Output Specifications

Documentation standards, like other types of standards, must be designed with local requirements in mind. Standards copied wholesale from a publication or from another organization are rarely completely successful. The standards presented here are for purpose of example. They are used and liked in the company they were written for, but that does not mean that they would be suitable for all installations. They could, however, serve as guidelines for developing new standards or revising existing ones.

Output Documentation Standards

1. Introduction

   All standards in this section are mandatory.

   Output must be specified in the following ways:

   a. Programming Layout (see Programming Standards Manual).

   b. Output Description Sheet (Exhibit 1).

   c. Output Specification Sheet (Exhibit 2).

   d. User Mock-Up

   Any output to be distributed to users must be approved in simulated report formats. These mock-ups are produced from the Output Specification Sheet, punched in cards, and run with "Printer Mock-Up" (see Software Support, Bulletin No. xx).

2. Applicability

   The output documentation described in this section is to be prepared for all reports and other hard-copy output distributed to users or data control staff, including remote transmission of hard copy; for VDU displays; and for turnaround documents handled at any time by users, including punched cards. It is not applicable to messages for computer or terminal operators or for any output, such as tapes and disks, that is recycled for system processing.

TITLE: OUTPUT DESCRIPTION SHEET	Page:
PREPARED BY:	Issue:
SYSTEM:	Date:
	Ref:

OUTPUT NAME:

MEDIUM:

SEQUENCE (if any):

RETENTION AND PROTECTION:

PROGRAM REFS:

SIZES   <u>Average</u>   <u>Maximum</u>   <u>Minimum</u>

CHARACTERS/LINE

LINES/PAGE

PAGES

HANDLING AND DISTRIBUTION

REMARKS

Exhibit 1   Output description sheet

3. Output Description Sheet—Exhibit 1

An Output Description Sheet is to be prepared for each report, display, or other output produced by the system as specified in (2) above.

The Output Description Form defines the output as follows:

Prepared by: Name of systems analyst.

System: Designated name and code of system.

Output Name: Designated name of output, for example, report name.

Medium: Device and medium, for example, line printer model xx hard copy, line-printer model xx litho master, VDU model xx.

Sequence (if any): for example, sort sequence for report lines.

Retention and Protection: Retention cycle and confidentiality classification, if applicable.

Program References: Number(s) of program(s) that produce output and use it as input, if applicable.

Sizes: Expected average, minimum, and maximum numbers of characters per line, lines per page, and pages; read "frames" for pages in the case of displays.

Handling and Distribution: A complete list of ancillary forms operations to be performed, including distribution to users.

Remarks: Must include a brief description of the purpose of the output; may also include comments on number of copies, special handling, preprinted forms, etc.

4. Output Specification Sheet—Exhibit 2.

An Output Specification Sheet is to be prepared for each type of line in the output described on the Output Description Sheet. Exceptions are heading and title lines, which are shown on the Programming Layout.

Prepared by: Name of systems analyst.

System: Designated name and code of system.

Output Name: Designated name of output from Output Description Sheet, plus name or number, or both, of this line of the output.

Spacing: Spacing to be performed *before* this line.

Conditions: If applicable, conditions under which this line appears on the output.

Field Name:

Print Positions: Or display line position or card column, as applicable; beginning and ending position numbers.

TITLE: OUTPUT SPECIFICATION SHEET				Page:	
PREPARED BY:				Issue:	
SYSTEM:				Date:	
				Ref:	
OUTPUT NAME:					
SPACING:					
CONDITIONS:					
FIELD NAME	PRINT POSITIONS	SOURCE	FORMAT & SIZE		EDITING

Exhibit 2   Output specification sheet

Source: Computer file, record, and field from which derived.
Format and size: COBOL or PL/1 picture or equivalent.
Editing: Detailed specification of editing requirements, such as zero suppression, insertion of punctuation, insertion of currency symbols, etc.

Bibliography

Anand, Valerie. 1973. How to by-pass the paperwork. *Accountancy,* February: 62–64.

Auerbach on Automatic Photocomposition. 1922. Philadelphia: Auerbach.

Beer, Gwen. 1965. *Machines for Office Workers.* London: Macdonald.

Canning, Richard. 1973*a*. Developments in data transmission. *EDP Analyzer,* March.

———. 1973*b*. Protecting valuable data—Part I. *EDP Analyzer,* December.

———. 1974. Protecting valuable data—Part II. *EDP Analyzer,* January.

Computer Management. 1970. Computer originated microfilm. June: 30–36.

Daniels, Alan, and Yeates, Donald, eds. 1969. *Basic Training in Systems Analysis.* London: Pitman.

Data Management. 1973. Copy service puts computer output on microfilm. April: 12–14.

Data Systems. 1972. The negative approach. September: 26–36.

Enrick, Norbert Lloyd. 1972. *Effective Graphic Communication.* Princeton: Auerbach.

Fürrst, Wolfgang. 1970. Reproducing computer printout. *Data Systems,* March: 26–29.

Goode, George E. 1973. Security for teleprinters and data communications. *Data Management,* January: 21–26.

Green, R. Elliot, and Parslow, R. D. 1970. *Computer Graphics in Management.* London: Gower.

Griffiss, G. L. 1971. A practical application of a generalized data entry and validation system for use in a mixed real-time and batch environment. *Computer Bulletin,* July: 254–257.

Hoffman, Lance J., ed. 1973. *Security and Privacy in Computer Systems.* Los Angeles: Melville.

Kerby, John M. 1973. Print production by computer. *Data Processing,* September-October: 310–313.

London, Keith R. 1973. *Documentation Standards,* 2nd ed. New York: Petrocelli Books.

McLaughlin, Richard A. 1973. Alphanumeric display terminal survey. *Datamation,* November: 71–92.

Milward, G. E., ed. 1962. *Organization and Methods—A Service to Management.* London: Macmillan.

Paller, Alan, and Berger, Samuel. 1970. A map is worth a thousand printouts. *Computer Decisions,* November: 38–41.

Parry, M. B. 1970. Data output peripheral devices. *Automation,* March: 37–40; June: 21–26.

Parslow, R. D., Prowse, R. W., and Green, R. Elliot, eds. 1969. *Computer Graphics—Techniques and Applications.* New York: Plenum.

Pike, Brian. 1973. How COM operates. *Computerware,* May: 8–10.

Pitts, Brian. 1970. Continuous paper chase. *Data Systems,* August: 18–21.

Preston, John. 1973. Applications in graph plotting. *Computer Weekly,* April 26:13.

Roberts, Hugh. 1973. Why COM? *Computerware,* May: 5–7.

Rubin, Martin L., ed. 1970. *Handbook of Data Processing Management.* Vol. 4, *Advanced Technology—Input and Output.* Princeton: Auerbach.

Skatrud, Ralph. 1969. A consideration of the application of cryptographic techniques to data processing. *Proceedings of the FJCC.*

Smedley, Jill. 1970. Multiple copy jungle. *Data Systems,* August: 22–25.

Smith, Graham. 1969. Some guidelines for the design of primary data vetting programs. *Australian Computer Journal,* May: 194–200.

Smith, T. G., and Pao, Y. C. 1973. *Introduction to Digital Computer Plotting.* New York: Gordon and Breach Science Publishers.

Smythe, Clare. 1971. Making top form. *Data Systems,* May: 24–26.

Swann, Cal. 1969. *Techniques of Typography.* London: Lund Humphries.

Taylor, Howard. 1973. COM information retrieval and computer software. *Computerware,* May: 11–12.

Van Tassel, Dennie. 1969. Advanced cryptographic techniques for computers. *Communications of the ACM,* December: 664–665.

Wainwright, Gordon. 1973. Can printout be more readable? *Data Systems,* June: 20–21.

Walley, B. H. 1968. *Manual of Office Administration.* London: Business Publications.

Wood, John. 1972. Computer output direct to microfilm. *Computer Bulletin,* August: 398–400.

Wooldridge, Susan. 1973a. *Computer Input Design.* New York: Petrocelli Books.

———. 1973b. *Software Selection.* Princeton: Auerbach.

Wooldridge, Susan, Corder, Colin R., and Johnson, Claude R. 1973. *Security Standards for Data Processing.* New York: Halstead Press.

Zaphiropoulos, Renn. 1973. Nonimpact Printers. *Datamation,* May: 71–76.

Index